Solamente en San Miguel

SOLAMENTE *en* San Miguel

VOLUME II

Forty-Two Writers
Capture the Magic of San Miguel

Jeanne Mills, Editor
Mary Katherine Wainwright, Submissions Editor
Carlos Soberman, Publishing Coordinator

PRODUCED BY THE SAN MIGUEL LITERARY SALA
SAN MIGUEL DE ALLENDE, MEXICO
SUSAN PAGE, DIRECTOR
WWW.SANMIGUELLITERARYSALA.ORG

Solamente En San Miguel — Volume II
Forty-Two Writers Capture the Magic of San Miguel
Collection Copyright 2010 by San Miguel Literary Sala, A.C.
Individual stories copyright by their respective authors
Published by Parroquia Press

ISBN 978-0-615-40952-8
9 8 7 6 5 4 3 2
First edition November 2010

Cover Design by Fran Schiavo
Interior design by Layla Smith (layladesign.com)
Project Coordination by Mary Katherine Wainwright, Jeanne Mills, and
Carlos Soberman

Printed in the United States of America

For information about film, reprint, or other subsidiary rights, or to
purchase multiple copies, please contact:
San Miguel Literary Sala
susan@susanpage.com

Parroquia Press
PMB 549
220 N. Zapata Hwy. #11
Laredo, TX 78043
Phone: 510-295-4097

Parroquia Press is a division of The San Miguel Literary Sala
www.sanmiguelliterarysala.org

Preface

Founded in 2004, the San Miguel Literary Sala gave visibility and voice to the many and various writers already plying their trade in studios overlooking stunning views, romantic courtyards, seedy bars or dusty pueblo paths. A magnet for writers ever since it became an arts enclave in the fifties, San Miguel has been home to many recognized literary figures: Neal Cassady, Vance Packard, Clifford Irving, Gary Jennings, Hal Bennet, Bill Wittliff, W.D. Snodgrass, Joseph Persico, Wayne Greenhaw, and Tony Cohan are just a few.

The programs produced by the Literary Sala include monthly author readings, which have showcased more than 400 authors in six years; a bookstore featuring the works of local authors; this anthology and the original *Solamente en San Miguel* — Volume I; Summer Literary Festivals, and an annual International Writer's Conference. We are proud to have hosted Barbara Kingsolver, Tom Robbins, John Berendt, Erica Jong, Rebecca Walker, Sandra Cisneros, Sena Naslund, and Josephine Humphreys, among many others, at events that have established San Miguel as a major literary destination commensurate with its status as a World Heritage Site.

This anthology is the product of hundreds of hours of time donated by enthusiastic and hard-working volunteers. The Sala expresses enormous gratitude to the Project Managers, Jeanne Mills, Carlos Soberman, and Mary Katherine Wainwright, and others who have contributed to the project: Diane Berman, Gerry Camp, Wayne Greenhaw, Marcia Loy, Natalie Parker-Lawrence, Fran Schiavo, Sharon Steeber, and Lulu Torbet. We also applaud all the writers who submitted work for consideration.

Susan Page
September 2010

Contents

In Memoriam

Lynette Seator
1929 - 2009

Lynette Seator's great charm, dignity, intelligence—and her bilingual skills—made her many friends in both the Mexican and ex-pat communities of San Miguel. Enthralled by Mexico during childhood visits, she went on to become Professor of Modern Languages at Illinois College. In 2003, she moved to San Miguel. Lynette's championing of minorities and the disenfranchised was reflected in her work, which appeared in numerous journals and in two published volumes of poetry, After the Light *(1992) and* Behind the Wall Poems *(1999). She edited two books of poems by inmates to whom she offered poetry workshops,* Hear Me Out: Poems from Prison *(1996) and* Speaking through the Bars: Poems by Women *(1999). In San Miguel, Lynette gave readings at the Authors' Sala and at the annual Poetry Festival. She mentored numerous young Mexican students.*

Collect Us

A gong on a pan is the music to
the coming of the garbage man.
Opening our houses and spilling us out,
he's the promise of delivery
from hour to hour dying. Peelings
and crusts, shells, bones, burned

bulbs, and what was
stripped from last night's love.
Our waste convenes us:
those born in beds behind these walls,
an old *gringo* new to the street,
families producing *prietitos* to diaper.

As I stagger down, refuse in tow,
orange stripes meet me en route
to relay my offering
to the man at the top.
Tall as a god on his trash truck,
he reaches down to take up
our garbage about
to bury its makers.

The Rebozo

Indian women I know
wind their babies in shawls
close to their bodies.
The child's eyes ride by
strangers, seldom
cry like yours behind bars
of a painted bed.

If you came back now
I would buy a blue *rebozo*
to wrap and carry you
tied to the swing of a day's work.
Warmed in its rhythm.

W.D. Snodgrass
1926 – 2009

W.D. Snodgrass received the Pulitzer Prize in Poetry for his first book, the ground-breaking collection, Heart's Needle *(Knopf, 1959). The author of numerous books of poetry, translation, and literary criticism, he received many awards, including the Harold Morton Landon Award for Translation for his* Selected Translations *(BOA Editions, 1994).*

Where's It Hot and Cheap?

That was the question my late husband, W. D. Snodgrass, asked in 1982 after learning he was up for a year's sabbatical from teaching. Savvy enough to query a well-traveled artist, he got turned in the right direction: San Miguel de Allende. After we learned what country it was in our search for a winter's escape ended, but we never imagined that first lengthy stay would be the beginning of a lifelong love affair with a town and its people.

In those pre-Google days, it wasn't easy finding solid information about getting to and staying in San Miguel, but once again luck was with us. Patricia Goedicke and her husband, Leonard Robinson, rented us their home on Recreo. We drove the 2500 miles (our Datsun's air conditioning conking out the moment we crossed the Texas-Mexico border), and our lives were never again the same.

It was a memorable first night in San Miguel, in large part because of the terrifyingly steep descent into town via the Salida a Querétaro, in first gear with the brake pedal pressed firmly to the floor. We found the house and, still dazed by the long drive around and over mountains dotted with crosses commemorating the myriad lives lost, walked the several blocks to the *centro*. The one guidebook I had found mentioned Mamma Mia's, where we went for pasta and wine. The food may not have been memorable, but the music was: there, on a small stage a few feet from our table, was El Lobo playing flamenco guitar music.

Since I'm writing to the converted, there's no need to describe how effort-lessly San Miguel works its magic: you come, you see, you're conquered. How many times through the years De and I would struggle to describe its every-day enchantments to friends up north, but how to communicate the quality of light on stone and *bugambilia*, the early-morning cacophony of roosters and church bells, the aroma of roasted corn, onions and *carnitas*? But beyond the town's sensual pleasures, we discovered deeper, more lasting satisfactions that come not from light and stone, birds and flowers, tequila and tacos, but, rather, from the people we met on a shared bench in the *jardín*, an adjourn-ing table in a café or restaurant, adjacent seats at the Wodin's bimonthly Shakespeare readings, play readings, concerts, and lectures.

And then there are the people who remain nameless, but whose faces you see, year after year, until you don't. For several decades, an old yet still hearty looking Mexican woman was a fixture in the *centro*. As the last stanza from De's poem, "On the Street," makes clear, begging was way beneath her:

> Proud
> of the meager Spanish
> I could manage, I offered,
> *"No tengo cambio"*
> in excuse.
> Peering up through lenses
> thick as signal lanterns
> frosted, long sunk underseas,
> she shot out one claw,
> snapping,
> "Go to the bank, then,"
> in good English.
> Which I did.

We thought we wanted someplace hot and cheap. Lucky for us, we got San Miguel instead.

Kathleen Snodgrass is the author of The Fiction of Hortense Calisher *(University of Delaware, 1993). With her her late husband, W. D. Snodgrass, she co-edited and co-translated several books of poems by the Romanian poet, Dona Rosu. Her translations of Mexican poets have appeared in such journals as* Poetry International *and* Northwest Review.

Walter Leo Meagher
1935 – 2010

Walter Leo Meagher was a writer and naturalist. His love for Mexico started when, as a young man, he rode through the Sonora desert on horseback, and was reignited on his honeymoon in San Miguel in 1986. Walter wrote two books, five monographs and 165 published essays about Mexican culture, the history of American higher education and natural history. He has contributed the Bird Sightings *series to the Audubon website and essays to* Atención, *as well as to the online San Miguel Botanical Garden's* Cactus Newsletter, *the* Oxford Magazine *(Oxford University publication), and* The Deddington News *(Oxfordshire). He was the author of the first complete inventory of the flora of El Charco Botanical Garden,* Flora of El Charco *(2007) and of* Wild & Wonderful *(2008). Walter was a life member of the ASPT (American Society of Plant Taxonomists) and a member of the BSBI (Botanical Society of the British Isles). Walter lived with his wife, Wendy, in England and San Miguel de Allende.*

Street Dogs in San Miguel

Having a wider range of acquaintances than dogs kept house-bound or on a leash, more buddies to visit, more liaisons to be initiated, San Miguel street dogs have a busy social life. The disadvantage: uncertainty. Where will they find food? Which dog will they have to fight for it?

Leash dogs are restricted, except when they are allowed to run in open spaces. Taken out to exercise their masters, they do their business and then return home. Rarely are they out for long. What they know best is the interior of a dwelling. Leash dogs know other dogs on regular routes and check the signposts for messages, but they may not dally. Masters and mistresses have other things to do, and so their dogs don't have the scope for friendships that street dogs have.

Dogs are native to the Americas, unlike the horse, cow, pig, donkey, and firearms. Perhaps they traveled with the first arrivals, hunters crossing the Bering land bridge. Aztecs raised dogs for the table and served them to Cortés and his men, along with turkey and tortillas. The Tlaxcalans, before becoming allies of the Spaniards, argued against this alliance on the grounds that they were men, not gods, as others had thought: *"...after all, they ate turkeys, dogs, bread and fruit."*

The Spanish arrived with dogs much larger than Aztec dogs, and with a different training. In Cortés' conquering army, dogs were numerous: *"...presumably either Irish wolfhounds or mastiffs. Dogs had fought effectively, and had been used brutally, in establishing other parts of the Spanish empire. Cortés would not have dreamed of depriving himself of their use. To the Mexica, the Castilians en route seemed a fearful sight. Their dogs went before them. They came panting, their noses in the air, their nostrils distended, the foam dripping from their mouths..."*

Most Mexicans are not sentimental about dogs. Mexico has no queen with ten corgis to set an example. A dog without a master is a dog without protection from a gratuitous kick, a target for stones thrown by idle boys. Periodically, the city rounds up these dogs and they never return.

Street dogs belong to San Miguel, without belonging to a person; they live knowing they may be abused. This gives them their look, unmistakable to the keen observer. Their eyes flicker between petition and resignation; they are often preoccupied with finding a meal and are utterly unused to leisure, so necessary for the cultivation of philosophy and the arts.

Many of the dogs in the Chorro district are residents of a home. In their social class positions, as well as in the parts they play in the society of our street (Calle Chorro), these dogs have specific duties. Many are confined to the home they are to defend and in which they languish. Some of these dogs are muscular, high-shouldered and thick-haired, the premier guard dogs of Calle Chorro. They have been raised to defend home or shop, and are commissioned to frighten everyone. Often they have the blood of a German shepherd.

At Las Quatro Milpas, when it was a small general store with eggs and mops, a guard dog prowled the roof, his fang-bared head reaching out over the edge. He was an animated gargoyle, sculpted to frighten the devil. He barked loudly, incessantly, ferociously, at each passerby for as long as it took one to walk the length of the shop and beyond. He was imprisoned on the rooftop, and I knew it, but I trembled at his ferocity nevertheless. He believed we were all wicked, and that every passerby would consent to a temptation for intrusion or any opportunity to trespass.

How different is the temper of the large German shepherd that lies in the doorway of the bicycle shop, its high-value products scintillating in the sunshine. He is on duty, you can be sure of that, but he is fast asleep, as if San Miguel were Cancún. In the more hot and humid season, he withdraws a little into the front room of the shop with its glistening metal machines.

Sunbathing is the way with most shop guard dogs. There is no more relaxing a sight in San Miguel than a smooth-haired medium-build dog, with outstretched legs and tucked back paws, sound asleep in the doorway of an electronic goods shop. These dogs are under the protection of St Francis of Assisi, relaxing in the mastery of their duties, which are little used, and confident they are valued for themselves. Small dogs may be guard dogs too; all dogs, we know, assume the role that induces their guardians to feed them. Perhaps dogs adopted man when, from the cave entrance, he threw gnawed bones into the fire-lit night and the scavenging pack found goodness in them.

There are more small dogs than large dogs in Chorro, but they are at home all day, peering onto the street from behind a barred window, and not posted on a watchtower or an open doorway. They thrive on the exhibition of a constant and jealous loyalty. The work of the night ends with a commonality of yowling before sunrise. The dog chorus is in unison before light suffuses the morning air.

Of small dogs, the most privileged are lapdogs. They are not a breed so much as a caste. Lapdogs are usually groomed and bathed by a professional. They may even be fed at the table and sleep on the bed of their owner. Lapdogs, a sub-category of which are boutique dogs groomed for walks on leashes, the dog and owner dressed as if for a photo shoot in *¡Hola!,* are at the other end of the continuum that starts with Mesolithic hunters (10,000-5,000 BC) domesticating wild dogs that prowled the midden and snatched uneaten fragments of food.

Small dogs, no matter what their breed, are more ill-humored when the owner leaves the home, because they are so much more a pet than merely a guard dog; they bark longer and in a more high-pitched voice than a mastiff or Great Dane, deep-voiced dogs, used to staying on the roof top, having a view of all the world, like a Telstar.

In the busy shopping hours before midday, one sometimes sees someone carrying a well-groomed white toy poodle in a pouch, permitting the greatest intimacy between beast and person. To anyone moved by a dog's friendly eyes and investigatory nose, this is an entertaining sight.

Chorro is a friendly street. The sidewalk is narrow and often interrupted by a telephone pole that takes almost its full width. Two persons approaching the impasse from different directions create the conditions for what can occur daily in England — intimidation. But not in San Miguel. One person will always give way with good grace. Man to woman; younger woman to older woman; youths to adults. In cases when a street dog is trotting along a sidewalk, the dog gives way to oncoming persons, without ever changing his pace and purpose. By nature, he is deferential, but for his deference he expects no gratitude.

Street dogs are known best by their pace and manner. They move steadily at a fast pace, and are certain of their short-term destination. They see you, but bend away from you. Their purposes arise from within themselves, waiting on no command, nor do they fawn for praise. Each is at liberty in the city he knows as if he were Magellan. They endure homelessness as a matter of right. They accept their plight. And they survive for as long as the dogcatchers can't find them.

Doors and Green Velvet

Cazz Roberts

*M*y mother never liked my half-sister; she merely tolerated her. My older sister, Manuelita, hated her. I loved her. I called her Yayita, though her real name was Geralda. I was nearly six years old when she came to live with us, and she was 12. I felt sad for her that day as she stood before the *zaguán,* her back to me, her head dropped forward, her mother gone. I knew her mother would never come back for her. I knew she was crying

It was January, 1902. Yayita and her mother had come with urgency to speak to my mother, the Señora Castillo. Eufemia, Mama's old servant, showed them into the small sitting room, the room of secrets guarded by heavy double doors. Some secrets leaked out through those thick doors, through the peep-hole too far down to be noticed by grownups. I squinched my eye into position and peeped in. On the patterned rug, I could see my mother's shiny white shoes, the ones with the strap that fit snug over the top of her foot. Across from them rested a pair of dull, black, thick-heeled shoes loosely filled with two socked feet, while scruffy brown boots with frayed laces swayed on tip-toes to and fro beside them.

The woman spoke, a muffled voice. Mama was silent. "I am dying, Señora...*me muero de la Tisis...*

"...the Consumption..."

"....all the way to San Miguel to bring her..."

"She is your husband's daughter." A cough, forced breath. No word from Mama.

"Have mercy, Señora. She is just a child."

"How dare you," said Mama finally. Her voice was harsh.

"...decent home...decent family...your bastard child..."

"...my husband is dead."

Some of these secrets stayed in my head until I was old enough to understand them. I scuttled back from the doors as they opened outwards, and dropped my doll onto the floor. The black-shoed woman fluttered out. A blue-gray *rebozo* covered her lower face. Her eyes were red, swollen. She rushed down the three short steps to the *zaguán*, and the grand wooden door that opened onto cobble-stoned San Miguel de Allende. The booted girl followed close behind. "Mama!" she called. The woman turned back. "You will be strong," she said. Her thumb marked a sign of the cross over the girl's forehead, over her lips, over her heart. She held her daughter, a furtive closeness. *"Adios m'hija,"* she said. *"Que Dios te bendiga y te acompañe."* God bless and be with you always. The woman wrapped her rebozo around her head and stepped outside.

My mother watched, straight and stern from the top of the steps. I picked up my doll from the tiled floor and placed her in the toy wicker carriage, straightened her blanket. I wanted to wheel her towards the splash of sunlight that covered the far edge of the corridor and the purple bougainvillea that climbed a column to the top of the house, but Mama's cold voice brought my head around to look and brought the strange girl's head around to face her.

"Eufemia!" said Mother. She cocked her head up, stretched tall. "Come for this girl. She will help you in the kitchen." The old woman took the three steps down to the *zaguán*, stood beside the girl, spoke quietly, plodded back up the stairs. The girl followed, eyes down-turned, limp, gray dress, orphaned. "And get rid of those disgusting boots," said Mama.

I wanted to ask Mama what the girl had done wrong, why the woman had given her away, but, even as a small child, I had noticed mama's recent intolerance for my questions. I was frightened to speak to her. She walked away without noticing me, rustled her long bustled dress along the portico to the sewing room.

Manuelita clacked over to me in her new shoes, and stood directly in my pathway. "Well, little sister," she said. She dug her fists into her hips and looked down at me with her 12-year-old smirk. "You'd better be careful. You might be given away one day."

I always believed I had done something to offend Mama, even before the day my half-sister arrived. I never understood her distant kind of love. Not that Mama's love was cruel, but certainly not affectionate. It was just a daily dole out of routine, delivered through an extension of herself, Eufemia. Doting mothers were weak, and children overly at ease with their parents were disrespectful. I often played with my dolls along the large, arched corridors, and grabbed Eufemia by the skirt as she hurried by on her way to the kitchen. I liked to stretch my arms out and twirl in a circle until I got dizzy and then wander along the corridor like a *borrachito*, a drunkard. Mama never liked that game.

One morning, as I pushed my doll carriage along the upper corridor, I peered in to my mother's bedroom. It was a large room with a three-mirrored dressing-table and a tall curtained bed, and an altar to the image of the Virgin of Guadalupe that hung from the wall just above the pillows. Mama was still in her night gown and a knitted *chalina* covered her shoulders. She sat on a chair next to her bed, fanning her face with her hand, while Eufemia squeezed water from a facecloth into a great floral bowl. My mother wiped all around her neck and face. The sick-bucket rested beside her. Was Mama sick? "Mama?" I asked. Her eyes widened as she caught me in her sight. Her bright pink face radiated anger.

"Downstairs with you, *niña!*" she said, her voice harsh. Eufemia came to the door and calmly pushed it closed. Numb outside my mother's room, I felt my tears gather at the base of my eyes and slowly fill my sight, until I could see only distortions of the door.

A blink emptied them out. I walked away.

The Angelus was a ritual at our house. The Parroquia bells rang it out three times a day, a call to devotion, to honor the Incarnation of God in Jesus Christ. At the noon-time call, we girls and my mother, the maids and any visitor who might be there, took our places in the formal sitting room. Some knelt. Some stood. All faced the large painting of the Dolorosa, the Virgin Mary at the most painful moment of her life, at the foot of the crucifix where Jesus, her son, *su hijo,* hands and feet nailed, died so we, his beloved Catholic followers, could be saved from all our sins. We prayed our Hail Marys, while Eufemia lit a long stemmed, metal oil lamp that sent a thread of black smoke up the wall to the hand-painted cloth sky that served as the ceiling.

One noon-time, shortly after my half-sister came, Mama didn't come down for the Angelus prayers. In fact, no one came. Only Manuelita and I stood together in the formal sitting room waiting for adult direction.

I climbed onto the green lounge, my back to the Dolorosa. I watched my fingers comb the velvety darkness, loosening the smell of undisturbed furniture. Manuelita sat at the edge of the rocking chair, feet together, silent, staring at me. Mama would be here at any moment. I looked out the door. Speckled sunlight bounced off the tiled floor, left its reflection in my eye. I ushered the reflection around the room, until it fell on Mama's *reclinatorio*, her prayer-stool. Where was Mama?

Manuelita rocked in the chair, squeaked back and forth in the chair, staring at me, her eyebrows gathered. I slid off the lounge and walked to the table where a glass cabinet held the baby Jesus on a satin cushion. I loved looking at the baby Jesus, the perfect baby Jesus, arms outstretched, just asking to be picked up. He was only brought out once a year, on the eve of Christmas, to be placed in the manger between his mother, the Virgin Mary, and Joseph, his earthly father, and a menagerie of animals and people of many sizes.

The room grew dark, then light again. Manuelita sat at the edge of the rocking chair, feet together, still staring at me. "Stop looking at me," I cried. "I want my Mamita. Why isn't she here for prayers?" Manuelita stood up from the rocker, drew her half-smile of satisfaction, straightened her skirt.

"Why would she want to pray with you?" she said.

From the sitting room doorway, alone, I watched the clouds close in for an afternoon storm.

A short, narrow door connected Mother's bedroom to ours on the upper level of the house. The door used to be open all through the night. I felt safe. I could hear my mother breathing. Manuela and I shared a bed, a wardrobe, a chest of drawers, though I never liked sharing my mother with her.

It was early morning when I sneaked out of bed. Mama's door was closed. She was quiet. The bursts of coughing were always worse during the night. I slid out into the corridor where rain puddles reflected moonlight. Rain usually didn't enter there, but a wind-driven storm could sometimes whip water all the way up to window level, where it then ran down the walls and leaked in under our bedroom door. The air was wet. The stone stairs were cold as was the cast-iron handrail led me down to the courtyard. I tippy-toed fast to the kitchen and the warm glow of lamp light.

Eufemia was surprised to see me at the doorway. "*Que hace, niña Juana?* What are you doing here? No shoes!" She motioned me to a blue chair at one end of the long, wooden kitchen table. "You'll catch your death," she said. "Give her some hot chocolate, Geralda, while I get her house shoes…and a brush for that wild hair."

I climbed up onto the woven grass seat. The chair blared back at me in red and orange painted flowers. The girl served the hot chocolate in a special little cup used only for that. It was short, wide. It had four feet and two delicate handles. I passed my fingers through the handles and brought the warm cup up to my lips. I inhaled the thick smell of chocolate and cinnamon, sipped slowly, put my cup down on its little saucer. My half-sister sat on the chair next to me and looked into my cup.

I asked her name, "*¿Cómo se llama?*"

"Geralda," she said.

"*¿Cómo? ¿*Yayita?" I sipped the chocolate.

"Ge-ral-da," she repeated.

"Ya-yi-ta," I repeated. Her smile broadened, broke open to reveal yellow teeth.

"*Si, niña* Juana," she said, "Ya-yi-ta."

Whenever my father's brother and his wife came to San Miguel to visit, Mother had the small sitting room prepared to receive them. Eufemia positioned a jug of *limonada* and *dulces* wrapped in colorful china paper neatly onto a crisp linen cloth on a wooden tray. She stationed this on the large side-board that also held my grandmother's silver crucifix and a candle on a plate. Manuelita and I followed a routine: a polite greeting, a curtsy, a choice of one sweet each and out we went. That day, Uncle Joaquin closed the doors on us. Manuelita ran upstairs to eat her sweet in peace, urged on, she said, by the sickening way I chomped at mine.

I sat on the tiled floor next to the double doors and the tiny peephole. I heard my uncle's voice. "The boys are well?" he asked. My mother drew in a long, restricted breath.

"Yes," she said. "They will come soon for a visit." The boys, my brothers, were sent away to school after my father died. Too much for my mother,

Uncle said. They needed a strong hand. Mama used to read their letters to us, but she stopped the day she stopped coming down for lunch with us.

My mother coughed, a boiling, gurgling cough, the same cough I could hear from my bed at night. I heard the swish-swish of my aunt's taffeta skirt, the ding of glass on glass.

My fingers were sticky from the *cocada*, a coconut sweet. I stuck both hands together like in prayer. Then, pried them apart and watched the stickiness pull at the skin as the fingers separated with a shuwa sound.

"So, Ignacia," my aunt asked, "is it *La Tisis?*"

La Tisisssss? I licked the sweetness from my inner fingers. *La Tisis.* I had heard that word before.

The peephole spilled another secret, a secret question from my mother's lips. "What about Juana?" I pressed my ear up to the gap in the door. Mama was talking about me.

My aunt spoke. "The girl...what does Juana call her? Yayita? Yes. Let her have Juana."

I didn't hear Manuelita coming. I only felt the fierce tug on my hair. She pulled me back. "What are you doing?" she whispered. She crouched down and looked in the peephole. *"¡Vas a ver con mi mama!"* she said. Her whisper turned caustic. "I'm telling Mama!"

She pushed me over with the back of her shoe as she turned the door knob to the sitting room. I lay on the blue and yellow tiled floor and cried. What would Mama think of me?

The Fiestas of San Miguel came and went, without Mama's presence. The statue of San Miguel Archangel made its yearly parade around the streets, visited the churches, returned to the Parroquia dressed in its recently finished stone façade. The crowds gathered in the town center to see the grand *castillo* of fireworks that spurted colored lights and whistling cartwheels into the sky. I found a *carrizo* cartwheel hoop in the courtyard of our home the next morning, cold and blackened. I got soot on my fingers when I wrapped it in a linen serviette and placed it in my treasure box.

The dim, enclosed bedroom became Mama's coffin. Doctors kept her confined, locked up in this small dark world, shut off from us and visitors. My sister and I were safe from infection, but not from fear and sadness. I roamed the corridors and rooms of the courtyard and the house. I looked for signs of her presence, her place in the sewing room, her prayer stool, her dining chair. All empty. I missed her during those days, as much as I ever did after she died, despite signs she was living: the routine of food trays three times a day, the periodic appearances of doctor and priest.

I saw my mother just once more before she died. She called us to her room, to stand at the doorway. My aunt knocked, then pushed the bedroom door slowly inward. Mama lay in her altar-bed, the Virgin of Guadalupe looking over her. Candles dulled by daylight, were ineffective in softening her image as she lifted her pale head and her feeble, bony hand to greet us. The effort induced a coughing fit, an uncontrolled, growled cough which she smothered in a large handkerchief. Eufemia rushed to my mother's side. My aunt closed the doors, but I managed to see the blood flood into Mother's handkerchief.

It was true.

They cough up blood until there is none left inside them.

Yayita took my hand and walked me away.

Cazz Roberts was born in Sydney, Australia, and has lived for 35 years in Mexico. The City of Celaya, Guanajuato, where Cazz taught English for over 25 years, has given her much to write about in terms of cultural wealth and history of her adopted home. She writes short stories, usually fiction, and poetry. While much of her work talks about her homeland, her current series of short stories concerns historical family narratives that illuminate the richness of Mexican culture from around the turn of the 20th century.

Memories of Stirling Dickinson and San Miguel

MARY ELMENDORF

In the summer of 1941, my husband, the late John Elmendorf, and I arrived in San Miguel de Allende with the first group of summer work-study students from the Putney School in Vermont. This was the first such program in San Miguel. It was under the supervision of Stirling Dickinson whose mother was a friend of the Putney School director. Stirling was then Associate Director of a new bilingual art school, the Escuela Universitaria de Bellas Artes, which was directed by Don Felipe Cossio del Pomar, a well-known Peruvian art historian. Stirling had assured us that rustic accommodations could be available for students at the ranch house of Pepe Ortiz, the famous retired Mexican bullfighter, which Don Felipe had purchased. Students would study Spanish and take art classes at Bellas Artes. And Stirling offered to arrange internships with local craftsmen.

We had to give up our jobs, my husband's as French teacher at Hopkins Grammar School and mine as a social worker for the WPA. Even though we would be earning much less money, John was intrigued by this and I was excited about the new adventure. We accepted the challenge and it changed our lives forever.

We left for San Miguel from New York City with only two students. It was a three-and-a-half day train trip. We arrived exhausted in San Miguel at about 2:00 am. As we stepped onto the dark platform, we were frightened when a man, his face half-covered with a bandanna, handed us a note from Stirling which said, "I waited for over three hours to pick you up personally. Instead, I have paid this taxi driver to take you to La Posada Las Monjas, where they're saving two rooms for you. I'll see you at breakfast in the dining room at the Escuela de Bellas Artes which is just around the corner." At the hotel, we were greeted by the sleepy concierge who took us to adjoining rooms, both smelling of damp plaster. One had bedsprings in it, the other only a mattress. Obviously, San Miguel was not quite ready for visitors! The boys offered us the mattress and they slept on the floor in their sleeping bags.

The next morning, as we entered the Escuela de Bellas Artes through a beautiful patio, a deer approached John who was having his morning cigarette, snatched it from his mouth and ran off with it.

As we looked around for a table, a tall, very slim man with a shy smile greeted us and introduced himself as Stirling Dickinson. While we ate, we asked him questions about San Miguel, the art school, places where we might intern and his life in Mexico. I think that he realized then that we were not just casual tourists, that we were people who were interested in learning. He soon lost his shyness and became very relaxed.

Before we left the beautiful Convento de la Concepción, Stirling suggested we go back to our hotel, have a siesta and then come up to his house, Los Pocitos, located at Santo Domingo 40. "Take a cab to the Santo Domingo Church, then walk up the steps the rest of the way. Bring your sleeping bags and luggage." At his house, Stirling invited the four of us to stay with him instead of going up to the Rancho de Bellas Artes as it had been planned. "John, you and Mary, my guest room is yours for the summer and the boys can have my studio which has plenty of space. You can all share the bath." (The bathroom was decorated with bawdy frescoes by Rufino Tamayo, David Alfaro Siqueiros, Carlos Merida!)

Stirling's home, Los Pocitos, had large patios on several levels that separated his bedroom, bathroom and kitchen from the living room and guest quarters. The upper patio had a waterfall from springs on the hillside which supplied the water to his house. A pool, beside a stone wall bench, overflowed into a fish pond on the lower level to the entrance to the guest quarters. From the bridge across the arroyo, one could see Stirling's vegetable garden and apple tree as well as his impressive orchid collection. It was very beautiful.

Stirling told us that, in 1937, he and Heath Bowman had bought the land, which had been an old tannery, for US$90. A large property, it had ruins on two sides of a barranca with a flowing stream at the bottom. After a few years, Stirling bought Heath's share when Heath joined the U.S. Foreign Service.

Stirling's black Great Dane, Junior, was taught by Stirling to pretend to be a bull with Stirling as the bullfighter. Junior, who slept in Stirling's room, was a regular customer at the butcher shop down the hill where he went alone for his daily portion of meat and bones which Stirling paid for by the month.

Stirling also had a small dog named Chorrito who not only picked his meat daily at the butcher shop, but attended every movie at the only theater in town. He delighted audiences as he raced down the aisle to challenge every animal which appeared on the screen. Once, Chorrito sneaked into the opening of the newly-restored Teatro Angela Peralta when José Mojica, well-known opera singer and Stirling's friend, was giving a special performance. When the curtain opened, Chorrito stood in the middle of the stage. He seemed to bow as everyone applauded.

One of Stirling's dogs became equally special to our family. In early 1954, soon after we had moved to our new home in Mexico City with our young children, Lindsay, and Susie, three young men wearing baseball caps arrived from San Miguel, one carrying a basket with a tiny Airedale puppy and a note from Stirling to Lindsay saying, "This puppy is for you, Lindsay. He's just the right dog for a boy like you." Chispas, as we called him, travelled from Mexico to Providence, Rhode Island with us in 1961 when John became vice-president of Brown University, then onto Sarasota, Florida where John was president of New College. Chispas spent his last five years sitting on our sea wall waiting to swim with the dolphins in Sarasota. Stirling often came to Sarasota to visit us. Chispas lived 18 happy years.

During our first summer in San Miguel, John apprenticed himself to a weaver, one of the Putney students apprenticed to a shoemaker and the other student apprenticed to a silversmith. I apprenticed to a master potter. I spent my mornings learning to throw pots and to make basic shapes. In the afternoon, I took Spanish classes. On the way back from class, I often peeked into the studio where artist Rufino Tamayo, on summer vacation from New York, was teaching painting to ten white-haired women. Rufino invited me to join the class, but I told him that I didn't have any paints or brushes and I knew nothing about painting. "Come in," he said. "Here are brushes and paints. I'll teach you." From then, my afternoons were special.

Felipe Cossio del Pomar, director of the Bellas Artes, and his delightful Cuban wife often entertained students, faculty and staff. We went on picnics by horseback to the hot springs at Taboada. I'll never forget how wonderful cold boiled potatoes tasted when they were unwrapped from large hand-woven napkins, which we had tied onto our wooden saddles.

One of our most unforgettable trips was an overnight visit to Guanajuato in an old pick-up with planks for seats and canvas on the sides which one would roll down in case of rain. There was no road so we had to drive down the riverbed hoping we'd arrive in Guanajuato before the rains came and the riverbed filled. It did rain, a downpour! We arrived sore and soaked. We stayed overnight and it rained all the way back to San Miguel. We were soaked again!

We went with Stirling and others to Patzcuaro and Lake Janitzio. Later, Stirling helped us plan a tour of Mexico via second class bus, sleeping in inexpensive Mexican hotels or *casas de huespedes,* and visiting market towns as far as Oaxaca, learning about the art and craft of Mexico, practicing our Spanish as we travelled

We went to Acapulco and, with a note of introduction from Stirling, stayed at Todd's Place in Pie de la Cuesta. We swam in the breakers and watched sharks swimming through the waves at sunset. Swimming there is forbidden now and tourists give money to young Mexicans who dare to swim!

After we returned to the Putney School at the end of the summer, Stirling came to visit us and gave a slide show about San Miguel to the entire school. As a result of his presentation. thirty students signed up for the following year's trip to San Miguel although the group was limited to twelve.

The draft board refused to allow John to leave the US, since, as a Quaker, he was registered as a pacifist. At 24, I knew that it would be impossible for me to handle the SMA group alone, but I agreed to go if the school would send an older woman from Putney to be in charge of evening activities for the students, three boys and nine beautiful girls.

And so the second Putney School summer program, in the summer of 1942, went smoothly, but the excitement caused by these striking young girls in jeans was unbelievable! This was at a time when there were almost no Americans in San Miguel. Stirling was the only American who lived there year-round. Once, we attended a bullfight in Mexico City, sitting on the sunny side where foreigners rarely sat. Nearly everyone in the section stood and applauded as the students walked to their seats.

At Stirling's invitation, I stayed again in his guest room which was wonderful after busy days supervising students and continuing my work in pottery and painting. He was always very gracious and we became life-long friends.

With Stirling's help, I found an abandoned house just above Los Arcos at the top of Santo Domingo, behind the entry gates to the ranch of the famous bullfighter, Pepe Ortiz. He had raised fighting bulls before it was purchased in 1938 by Felipe Cossio del Pomar. Don Felipe entertained many important visitors here as well as students. Señor Ortiz's house, recently renovated, is now the Hotel Rancho Atascadero.

Los Arcos was the main gate to the ranch. I climbed up the hillside to look at the old aqueduct which channelled fresh water from the springs above it to the church of Santo Domingo and to various fountains. Above the aqueduct, there was a stone building that consisted of a large oblong structure with three-foot thick walls and a smaller structure attached. There was a bubbling spring just beside the building. Down below, by the arches, there was another small building, the former gatekeeper's office. I asked Stirling if he thought that Don Felipe would sell these buildings to me. The next day, Stirling and I went to see it.

The door to one building opened into a lovely small, dark room with 14-foot ceilings held by beams. This was a kitchen that had three charcoal burners. It was attached to a larger building, the actual house, on the northern side, which created a lovely sunny patio. It seemed the perfect refuge from the war, which was threatening to disrupt our lives and everyone else's. I thought that John and I could escape the outside world here.

Don Felipe offered to sell me the property from the aqueduct to the edge of the hillside by the spring, 279 square meters. It was called "El Paraiso" on the original deed from Pepe Ortiz to Felipe Cossio del Pomar. In 1942, I made my agreed payment of US$50, all of my savings!

Back at the Putney School in the fall of 1942, I became very depressed after a miscarriage and John urged me to return for the winter term at Bellas Artes while he continued teaching at Putney. I left for San Miguel on the train just after Christmas, 1942 and stayed until March, 1943 when I received a telegram from John: "Hurry home, I'm being drafted."

During that winter in San Miguel, I began renovating my hillside retreat. The first thing I did was to knock out a section of the west wall which faced toward San Miguel. I used those stones to install a terrace with seats and small steps leading down from the corner to the alley. I added a picture window, just like the one in Stirling's living room. The renovation cost US$125, all that I had.

I invited Stirling and his parents for a house warming on my new terrace from which we could see the Parroquia and the mountains and Stirling's house and orchid garden. Two pictures that Stirling's father took of the bare hillsides of what are now Atascadero and Los Balcones are still hanging in my San Miguel living room.

We did not come back to San Miguel at all from March, 1943 to Thanksgiving, 1950. In 1947, we went to the University of North Carolina in Chapel Hill to continue our graduate studies and start our family. In November, 1949, John accepted a position in Mexico City as the Director of the Instituto Mexicano Norteamericano de Relaciones Culturales, part of the US Embassy's Cultural Affairs section. This was partly as a result of glowing recommendation from Heath Bowman, with whom Stirling had written *Mexican Odyssey.* I was as excited as John. I would see old friends and learn to know Mexico more fully. And, important to me, we could visit my little refuge in San Miguel which John had never seen.

In November, 1950, nearly eight years after my last trip to San Miguel, we finally returned to Mexico with our two small children, excited about having Thanksgiving with Stirling, who had invited us to take over his guest quarters again. The first thing we did after Thanksgiving dinner was to walk up Santo Domingo through Los Arcos to our little house. To our horror, all the doors had been removed and taken, as well as the beams which had held up the roof. The thick walls were still there, but every improvement I had added in 1943 had disappeared, except for the terrace. I broke into tears, but Stirling said, "Don't worry; I can help you fix it up so that it's better than it was."

In 1946, Señor Campanella had purchased the Rancho de Bellas Artes and the Art School from Don Felipe who returned to Peru. During much of the 1950s, there was friction between this new owner and Stirling and the teachers. In the middle of the night, Stirling and most of the foreign teachers were picked up without warning, put in a boxcar and deported to the U.S. The school was shut down.

This was during the Joe McCarthy days, so few people in the American Embassy were able to help, but the Canadian Embassy and painter David

Alfaro Siqueiros helped obtain permits for the deportees to return to San Miguel. After several confusing months, the Instituto Allende was created, buildings were acquired and accreditation arranged so GIs could continue receiving their allotments. The new school flourished.

Soon afterwards, *Time* magazine accused Stirling of being a communist and a homosexual. His family lawyer sued *Time* magazine and won. *Time* printed a simple retraction, "*Time* erred."

Meanwhile, in Mexico City, at the Instituto de Relaciones Culturales Mexicano Norteamericano, my husband, as Director, had exhibitions by artists from San Miguel, including Leonard Brooks and Jim Pinto. But soon after, John and the Cultural Attaché at the U.S. Embassy, were accused of communism and blacklisted by Joe McCarthy. John was not allowed to complete his assignment as Director of the Instituto and spent over a year trying to clear his name without success. Fortunately, I had accepted a job as Director of CARE in Mexico, so I was able to support the family until he returned to academia. He was soon to be Dean, and later Vice-President, of Mexico City College where he stayed until 1960 when he became Vice-President of Brown University.

From 1975 to 1979, I made many visits to San Miguel, checking on things at Santo Domingo 48 as I finished my various work assignments in Mexico. I usually stayed in Stirling's guest room. By the summer of 1979, John and I were finally able to spend two wonderful months in San Miguel together. Our house was nearing completion, but, once again, I accepted Stirling's invitation for us to stay with him, since there was not yet furniture in the house. Stirling took us to Adjuntos del Rio where we ordered furniture made of mesquite. That was John's last trip to San Miguel before he died of a heart attack in February, 1980 at the age of 64.

The last time I saw Stirling was in September, 1998 when he invited me to a Sunday picnic with the Grimaldi family. Stirling was then 88 years old. That evening, as he slowly climbed the 77 steps to my house for supper, he said, "My last walk up this hill. We'll have to get a ski lift or something like that. I'll check into it for you." As we enjoyed supper together, we decided to start a joint journal of shared memories of the 40's and 50's, some of which I have described here.

A month later, in October, 1988, Stirling was killed in a dreadful accident when his car plunged backwards down a precipice as he was turning around after attending a board meeting for one of the many charitable organizations he was working for.

When a news of this reached me, I immediately wrote a Letter to the Editor of *Atención* which was published in early November 1998:

> What a tragedy this is, but what a blessing to have such a vital, vigorous person as Stirling Dickinson escape long bedridden days. I'm very sad that I can't be there in San Miguel to share with all of you, whose lives he has touched in so many ways as he did mine and my family, our memories of this great man. It was Stirling who introduced us to the many worlds of Mexico: the world of arts and crafts, the excitement of travel by second class bus, train, and even in pick-up truck. But most of all, he introduced us to the Mexican people whom he loved and respected - for their creativity, their humor, their caring ways. He showed us the beauty in the off-the-road places — hidden ravines and brooks
>
> If we had not met Stirling, our lives would have been very different, much less full of adventures and experiences and a continuing return to San Miguel to be with Stirling again, to have him know our children and grandchildren, one of whom is named Stirling, to whom I gave my autographed copy of Stirling's Mexican Odyssey with its wonderful woodcuts and great descriptions.
>
> Sixty years ago, it was Stirling who turned all of us Elmendorfs into Latin Americanists at heart and aficionados of San Miguel de Allende. There is no way to thank him enough for helping San Miguel continue to be the wonderful community it is in spite of the enormous influx of outsiders — from the USA and Canada, but also from other parts of Mexico. Let's remember how Stirling lived his life, so filled with the joy of sharing.

Dr. Mary Lindsay Elmendorf has a BA Psychology, an MA Social Work and a PhD in Anthropology. She has worked as a teacher, a Quaker volunteer, as the Director of CARE in Mexico and as consulting anthropologist to the World Bank, the US Agency for International Development, the United Nations Development

Program and the World Health Organization. She received the Margaret Mead Award in 1982 . She was co-recipient of the Nobel Peace Prize in 1947. Brown University and the University of North Carolina each awarded her an Honorary Doctoral Degree. Mary has participated in all of the United Nations Conferences on Women, the 1978 UN Conference on Water and the 1992 Rio Earth Conference. She has written 13 books and many influential reports and papers. She married the late John Elmendorf in 1937. After his death in 1980, Mary married fellow anthropologist John Landgraf with whom she now lives in Sarasota Florida. Mary has two children, nine grandchildren and four great-grandchildren. She comes to her house on Santo Domingo as often as she can.

San Miguel de Allende

JULIETA CORPUS

Repiquetean las campanas
Con estrindente despliegue
Desde la bella Parroquia
Del Arcangel San Miguel;
Y un puñado de palomas
Alzan el vuelo azoradas,
Salpicándo el panorama
De aleteos color de miel.
Frescas brisas matutinas
Que despiertan mis nostalgias,
Remontándome a un pasado
Lleno de tranquilidad.
Niñez que guardo con celo
En un rincón de mi mente
Para esas noches sin calma
Que amenazan esta paz.
Cada piedra en cada calle
Va saturada de magia
Que se filtra fácilmente,
Atrapando al corazón.
Y sonríen las bugambilias
Desde los altos balcones
Al observar como todos
Van declarando su amor!

San Miguel de mis ensueños,
Sagaz ladrón de suspiros,
Desde Cardo hasta Loreto
Voy dejando en tí a mi ser.
Noches de mariachi en vivo
embriagando a los presentes
Con canciones de ésta Tierra
A la que un día he de volver.
Pido a Dios por Carmelita,
la vendedora ambulante
que hace ya más de dos años
conocí en esta ciudad.
Gente linda como Mario,
Quien ya es mi hermano del alma,
Permanecenerán conmigo
Por toda una eternidad.

San Miguel de Allende

Bells peal,
A strident deployment
From the beautiful Parroquia
Of the Archangel Michael;
And a fistful of doves,
Alarmed, rises into flight,
Splashing the scene
With their honey-colored flutter.
Cool morning breezes
awaken my nostalgia,
Take me back to a past
Filled with tranquility
And a childhood I jealously guard
In a corner of my mind
For the restless nights

That threaten my peace.
Every stone in every street
Is saturated with a magic
That so easily seeps into
And traps the heart.
Bugambilia smile
From high balconies
Upon observing how everyone
Goes about, declaring their love!
San Miguel of my dreams,
Shrewd thief of sighs,
From Cardo to Loreto,
I leave in you, my whole being.
Nights of live Mariachi bands,
Intoxicating their audience
With songs from this land
To which I must one day return.
I pray to God for Carmelita,
The street vendor
Whom I met in this city
More than two years ago.
Beautiful people, like Mario,
Who is now my soul-brother,
Will remain with me
For all of eternity.

— Translation by Laura Juliet Wood

Julieta Corpus is originally from Rio Bravo, Tamaulipas, Mexico. Her poems have appeared in various magazines, newspapers, and college journals such as, Tendiendo Puentes, The University of Texas Pan American Gallery Magazine, Interstice, *and* Tierra Firme. *She has been published in local newspapers, such as* The Mesquite Review *and* The Monitor's Writer's Edition: Festiba. *She has participated in the Rio Grande Valley International Poetry Festival for two years in a row, and her poetry is included in both anthologies. In 2009, Julieta was invited to be a guest poet at FELISMA in San Miguel Allende. She currently resides in Weslaco, Texas with her boyfriend Dale; and, for the past year, she has been the emcee for Poetry Nights at Savory Perks. She's an elementary teacher at Bowie Elementary while pursuing her MFA in Creative Writing at the University of Texas Pan American.*

Quiet

Jay W. Vogt

J came to Mexico to learn Spanish and to write. When my wife and I looked at houses to rent, I liked the one with the little studio perched up on the roof. Nice writing space, with views, and light. Quiet.

Before we signed our lease, I walked over and stood on Calle Murillo after dark, gazing up at the house. The sky was black, the stars sparkled, and the house was aglow with the light of street lamps. After hours, still quiet. We'll take it.

It wasn't long into our stay before I realized how unquiet our new home in centro really was. I'm not talking about church bells or fireworks, but cars and trucks laboring under our windows, a maid's radio next door on loud enough so she could hear it throughout the empty house as she cleaned, the three little Scotties who lived on the roof across from our bedroom and barked incessantly at anything that moved — all day long.

But this is Mexico, and I'm going with the flow.

The empty house on our other side, away from the maid, leaped to life with sound one morning as four workmen took pick axes to the rock hillside that bounded one corner of the home's grand open patio, just below my studio. The rocks rang out in protest, bitterly. I gazed down at them, two floors below, from my little writing studio feeling equal parts admiration and shock. If they planned on reducing this escarpment to dust, it was going to take a very, very long time. And so it did.

For months, the four workmen heroically and rhythmically hacked away at that hill. Who could begrudge them the radio that they played to make their hard work a little less hard? Now the maid's radio had a friend, and, like birds, they sang to each other all day long, right through me.

This is Mexico, and I'm going with the flow.

All this rock debris had to go somewhere. A young man would load it into a wheelbarrow, roll it through the patio, and dump it in the front hall. So as not to disrupt the traffic on tiny Murillo, the workers removed the rock chunks at 5 in the morning, heaving shovelfuls into the battered rear bed of an old pickup truck. Every shovelful clanged and caromed. The groaning truck was parked under our bedroom window, just above their handy exit.

This is Mexico, and I'm going with the flow.

My daughter's bedroom was at the back of the house, next to the rock cavity slowly emerging out of the hillside next door. The wall behind her bed was the same rock they were excavating, so she could feel every chip. Loose plaster from the ceiling sprinkled her bedspread.

This is still very much Mexico, and I'm still very much going with the flow. But now I'm afraid that they might break through the wall into my daughter's bedroom. I ask my landlady to have José, her maintenance man, check it out. Suddenly: my moment of weakness. For months, I've been soldiering through the radio sound the way the workers have been soldiering through the rock. I've learned to write with earplugs on. I've been going with the flow. Then I cave: "And while José is next door, can he ask them to turn the radio down?"

He does. And he goes away. Now the workmen turn the radio up — way, way up. It is positively screeching. No *gringo* is going to tell them what to do, not even through a Mexican.

My wife, who grew up in Mexico, says to me, "You should never tell a Mexican man what to do. He is too proud." Now she tells me. I feel contrite and angry. I want to go next door and stammer an apology — and sneak in at night and smash the radio. Day one goes by. I am a shamed, haunted, angry man. Day two. I can't be in the house. Day three. My studio, full of noise, mocks me.

Finally my wife, who speaks perfect Spanish, asks the boy, who is rolling the wheel barrow with rock back and forth below our wall, this simple question: "Would the workmen please lower the radio back to where it was before?" He takes this message with him as he slowly rolls his barrow back to the work area.

As suddenly as it began, the assault ends. The radio is turned not down, but off.

Days go by, and the workmen work on in silence, only the sound of ax against rock. Months go by, and the radio never gets played again.

Part of me is giddy. I want to buy some beer to leave as a peace offering over the wall, but my wife counsels "Leave well enough alone." I follow her lead.

Part of me is humbled. These men were strong enough to show me who was boss. And gallant enough to sacrifice what little they had for a lady. Part of me is sad. I still didn't know these men, and they remained hidden to me behind their great big walls.

We travel to appreciate other cultures, but sometimes it seems we just disturb them. Meanwhile, stoic as ever, the rock clung to the hillside, resisting their blows. The workers were still at it when our six months stay in San Miguel — not so quietly — came to an end.

Jay W Vogt is an organizational development consultant for entrepreneurial non-profits and mission-driven companies. He founded his practice, Peoplesworth, in 1982. Jay writes regularly about business. He published Recharge Your Team — The Grounded Visioning Approach with Praeger *in 2009. His first digital book,* Life or Death Lessons from Extreme Teams, *will be published by New Word City in 2010. Jay lives in Concord, Massachusetts, which, like San Miguel, is a renowned artistic, literary and spiritual center, as well as being the birthplace of its country's revolution. Jay's wife, Stephanie, was born and raised in Mexico City and together they bought a ruin in San Miguel's* centro *in 2004, during the visit chronicled in "Quiet," and renovated it. Their daughter now attends Colorado College.*

A Courtyard in San Miguel

MARY KATHERINE WAINWRIGHT

I sit at my small desk on the second floor. My red house sweater covers my shoulders to take away the chill of the morning air. Wall to wall windows and doors overlook a small balcony above the courtyard. The early morning sky is blue and clear of the clouds that will come later in the afternoon. Orange flame vines, blue plumbago, fuchsia bougainvillea, and a few red and pink geraniums fight for prominence on the walls and fences. The little green hummingbirds don't distinguish among them. All flowers are feasts to them, and they twitter and chitter as they move from flower to flower, color to color. I watch. I should be writing, but I watch, while my computer screen blinks white and blank. When I rented this *casita* in San Miguel de Allende, Mexico, I was sure this very scene would be a source of inspiration. I envisioned writing away my mornings, going downstairs only for an occasional cup of tea. I even hired a dog walker so I wouldn't have to leave my desk until later in the day.

Yolanda, the housekeeper, enters the courtyard. She is slender and slight. With my large bone structure and extra weight, I make two of her. She has long black shiny hair that she usually wears pinned up or in a single braid down her back. But twice I have seen her with her hair cascading down her shoulders, straight and sleek. Yolanda usually wears jeans, a cotton shirt, and a sweater that she sheds by noon. She walks slowly to the washing machine tucked away by the back wall and hidden from view by bamboo shades. She looks up. She knows I will be there writing. She waves and calls out, "*Buenos Dias, Señora.*" I wave in response. I turn to my computer. The noise of the washing machine beginning to agitate glides past my ears. I am deep into writing.

After a while, another sound intrudes into our peaceful courtyard. It is neither the soft voice of Yolanda nor the familiar whir and swish of the washing machine. This voice is a deep voice, harsh and masculine. He comes up to the fence my landlady erected to keep my pups from bothering the other tenants and calls out to Yolanda, "*Hola. Buenos días.*" This is Miguel, the gardener. His shoulders are wide and sturdy, and he wears a faded Abercrombie navy blue polo shirt and a red baseball cap. His hands are rough from work, but he is a gentle man. He does not look up to wave at me. The two of them rule here with impunity.

I once moved a potted geranium in the courtyard so I could see it from my desk. Someone moved it back. Several little clay and pottery animals are stacked in the corner by my front door. One day I arranged them in a harmonious grouping, the rabbit snuggling close to the frog, the snake rearing its head behind them. The next day they were stacked close together again, their backs against the wall. So I got the message. The garden, the courtyard, my casita, my neighbors' casitas in this small complex all belong to them. Even inside. Yolanda does not like for me to leave my shoes on the floor, and I have to look for them after she's been here to clean — under the bathroom sink, on the closet shelf. I believe she disapproves of my sloppiness.

This morning the two of them engage in animated conversation. They gesture with their hands toward the neighbor's impatiens, toward the plumbago that the wind tore down in the last storm, toward a few empty clay pots stacked by the bodega. I imagine they are either agreeing or disagreeing on the next gardening project. I have asked for some flowers for my balcony. My neighbors have beautiful pots of impatiens and geraniums. I would like some too. I hold my breath. Maybe they are deciding what they will move upstairs to my balcony. Yolanda turns and gestures towards me and my balcony. I was right. They *are* discussing me. I scrunch up my eyes and wish for a potted bougainvillea, deep fuchsia. Will I get the flowers? Or is she complaining because yesterday I moved the little frog to the other side of the courtyard to rest at the feet of the miniature roses? I do not know because I can not understand their conversation, their language. I am a stranger here in this world of Yolanda and Miguel, an interloper, a transient shadow moving across the surface of their existence, a stubborn obstacle that they have to sweep around until, like others before me, I too depart, and leave this courtyard to the rightful gardeners.

I return to what I know, black words marching across a blank white screen.

Mary Katherine Wainwright, a retired professor of literature and creative writing, moved to San Miguel in the spring of 2009. Her poetry has been published in Kalliope, Phoebe, Sarasota Review, Florida English Journal, Harp Strings, *and other small literary journals. She is the author of several published essays on Zora Neale Hurston and the Harlem Renaissance. This is her first creative nonfiction publication.*

Artist's Proof

Ellen Lurie

August 1992 San Miguel de Allende:
A body is found on a back street in the middle of the night — a white male approximately fifty years old. He was a peripheral figure in San Miguel, always around and alone. You've seen him. Everybody has. He was described as having been a painter, not extraordinary in San Miguel. I didn't follow the story. I have never heard anything else about him or about the circumstances of his death. I said a prayer for him that he rest in peace. That night I dreamed of bodies advertised in the lost and found section of the newspaper, items waiting to be claimed.

July 1992 San Miguel de Allende:
I sit on a lacy wrought iron bench, dozens of which follow the perimeter of this square. Treetops are clipped like hedges into cylinders of foliage balance on twisted trunks. Behind me, and across the cobblestone street, stands the Spanish colonial Palacio de Gobierno. The structure is crowned by the symbol of Mexico in stone relief, an eagle perched on a cactus bough, a serpent writhing in its beak. On either side of the *jardín,* across the stone streets, arched columns rise to form a sheltered walkway. Banks and stores now occupy seventeenth-century buildings that were once the homes of Spanish *gachupín* counts and wealthy *criollos.* Lemon morning light creeps over this graceful town.

A teenage Mexican boy peddles plastic Ninja Turtles rolling on wheels that make a loud, grating, cricket-like noise as they turn. He's catering to the Mexicans with these wares, as well as with the clouds of plastic balls and balloons suspended from a pole carried over his shoulder. The peddler gets competition from an even younger boy selling Batman figures of the same design as the Ninja Turtles. As they parade in endless circles around the plaza, the cricket-like noise is heard in syncopation. A group of Indians from the state of Michoacán arrive. The men sell brightly colored baskets and paintings on *amate*, tree bark paper. The women and children sell handmade cloth dolls and beaded necklaces.

A man with a gray ponytail and a backpack emblazoned with the Ying Yang symbol greets a tanned woman with a tattoo of Saturn on her upper arm. "Don't walk around the *jardín* too many times or you'll get dizzy," he cautions. She seems to be thinking this over.

Pigeons impassively observe the scene from perches high on the pink stone-work of the Parroquia. A statue of Ignacio Allende, a father of the Mexican Independence movement, and several statues of saints inside the Parroquia's iron gates complete the wordless spectators of this morning's activity.

July 1992 San Miguel de Allende

I arrived yesterday. It was hard for me to leave New York. The Mexicana jet's pulling up off the runway at JFK felt to me like a violent act, as if I were being ripped from the earth to which I am bound by flesh, and bones, and blood. I realized that my fear of flying has little to do with planes.

July 1992 San Miguel de Allende:

This morning, I saw the blind beggar who I have seen in all my years of visiting here. He sat crouched on the sidewalk where he has always sat; outside the colonial building that used to be the Aldama movie theater. He has not moved since I saw him last. I remember watching Mexican westerns in that theater, smoking and sitting on metal folding chairs with "Corona" painted across the back rest, thirteen years ago.

July 1992 San Miguel de Allende:

The green copper bells of the Parroquia sound the quarter hour. I walk behind Julio toward the French Park because the sidewalk, made of large smooth paving stones, is so narrow. I look at the back of his head. There are a few gray hairs. He is just in his mid-thirties. I look down to the heels of his leather boots. I say to myself, "This is your husband," and the words seem to come from a distant place. And I know he will not be my husband much longer.

August 1992 San Miguel de Allende two nights, two dreams:

One. I have a matte knife. I press the extended triangular blade into my mother's arm. I withdraw the blade. Blood begins to flow. Without emotion, I press the blade into a different spot on her arm. Blood streams out. I'm suddenly not sure if this person is my mother or my father. I want a gun. I am surprised that she/he wants one too; surprised that this person wants to harm me as much as I want to harm her/him.

Two. I am sleeping in Julio's room. (In fact, I am.) A noise awakens me. I get up and go to the door. Julio is speaking to me from outside the door, but I can't hear him. I open the window in the upper part of the iron and glass door and he says, "Don't open the door." I look into the bathroom and there hangs an effigy, a body made of stuffed clothing. It does not have a head or legs. It may not have arms. It swings slowly in a marked silence. Julio has gone up to the roof in pursuit of the source of the noise. He thinks he's helping by investigating. He doesn't know he has abandoned me to the swinging torso.

June 1979 San Miguel de Allende:

I am a teenager. My parents have permitted me and my best friend, Catherine, to come here with me to study art. We take silver class. I love the soldering torch. I make silver beads and concentrate as I solder the halves together. I have studied French — never Spanish. So we take Spanish too.

We live on Quebrada Street in a big crumbling house a couple of hundred years old. We rent a room from Libby, the American renter (we think) of the house. We can't imagine her owning anything. She is a bony, shadowy woman of about forty, older than any person teenagers would notice. We play soccer in the street with the pre-teen neighborhood boys.

We wake up and walk to Instituto Allende. Almost every morning, one or the other, or both of us, barely make it to the school before being overwhelmed by the need for a bathroom. The bathrooms at Instituto Allende have no toilet seats. They have no toilet paper.

Eventually we go to a pharmacy. We point to our stomachs and act out serious pain. This is not just normal diarrhea. The pharmacist offers us some vials, syringes and hypodermic needles. I don't know why we buy them. We go back to the house on Quebrada and check out the drugs and the paraphernalia. We look at each other seriously, questioningly — and then start to laugh. We throw the stuff in the garbage.

Our bathroom has a green tiled bathtub. I decide to take a bath. I turn on the faucet and nothing comes out. I call Catherine. We've never had to fix anything in our lives. We'd never pushed a button or flipped a switch that didn't promptly provide the expected result — until now. We do what we can, but no water. We think it must be us. I bend way over the tub and peer up into the faucet. It is dry. And then a big, brown scorpion crawls out. We jump back, scream, hop around, run out and collapse in laughter on the lumpy bed.

We hate San Miguel. But, little by little — *poco a poco* — it begins to get into our blood. I begin to love the tilted floor of our room (questions regarding the structural integrity of the building do not enter my mind). I love the chipped, clay tile. I love the cracked wall, the uneven stones, the rain-swollen wood, the carved *cantera*. The oldness of everything gives comfort, a sense of permanency. Everything feels somehow human; not perfect, not rational, sometimes so warm, sometimes cruel or indifferent. Everything has come tremendously alive.

July 1979 San Miguel de Allende:

Catherine and I go to the bar, La Cucaracha, on the *jardín*. "I need a light," I pantomime to a handsome, young Mexican. Julio pulls out a wax-coated match from a box of Clásicos, bends towards me and lights my cigarette. I say, "*Gracias.*" This single word accounts for about 20% of my knowledge of Spanish. He smiles and I see black-lashed eyes and a wide, white smile. One of the bottom teeth is crooked and this makes him even more attractive.

July - August 1979 San Miguel de Allende and Veracruz:

Julio knows when it is going to rain. He can smell it. This amazes me because the sky is blue. And his skin is cinnamon. And his eyes are black. We take his Great Dane to run in the thorn tree and cactus-dotted countryside. I take a picture of him wearing a straw cowboy hat which shields his face from the sun, drinking milk from a carton with his head thrown back.

Catherine meets some people and goes to Oaxaca with them.

Julio takes me to Veracruz on the bus to visit his older brother and wife. I love Mexican buses and especially traveling at night. We board and I move the side of my body against Julio's so that there are no open spaces between us. The bus driver plays his *ranchero* music which he interrupts to play a completely incongruent song. The Beatles' "Let It Be" fills the rocking bus. The violence and traumas of my young life pass through my mind. But I am able to let it be — to let it all be. Then the *rancheros* continue. I sleep cocooned against Julio as the bus bumps and sways and tumbles toward Veracruz.

We arrive in the morning. Julio's brother and wife are not happy to see us — or maybe just not me, the *gringa*. That night they put us up on their living room couch. It doesn't pull out. We end up on the floor. We try to keep things quiet, but, soon after, we hear sympathetic creaking from their bed.

We go to the first year birthday party of their first child, a girl. I find babies uninteresting. The party is at the maternal grandparents' house. They live in a *vecindad* down an alley behind a main street in the suffocating humidity and gasoline smells of a Veracruz summer. The party goes late (the birthday girl is not really the centerpiece of the festivities). We spend the night there in an unused room across the alley. Rats skitter around all night. The next day, we go to the beach and my Fred Braun pocketbook is stolen while Julio and I languish in the dark, leaden gulf sea.

August 1992 San Miguel de Allende:

I work in the printmaking studio of Instituto Allende and watch the acid eat away at the areas of my zinc plate that I have purposely left unprotected in order to etch my image. The surface of the zinc slowly bubbles until I reach my bare hand into the tray and lift the plate at an angle. The acid and water solution runs down the plate. I move the plate to the open faucet, rinsing it and my hand. I remove the acid resist layer with paint thinner. I wash the plate with soap and water, dry it. The work absorbs me in every step precluding all feelings except physical sensation. I am unaware that this process is a consolation.

I apply a soft ground to resist the acid bath and continue creating my image. I gently place delicate green *huizache* tree leaves on top of the uniform soft ground. They are fragile leaves that grow beside the *huizache's* strong, sharp thorns. I rest the plate on the press bed and cover it with paper followed by a thin felt blanket and two thicker ones. I run the plate through the press. I lift off the blankets and paper. I carefully remove the leaves which have broken the surface of the soft ground leaving a silvery filigree imprint. I etch the tenuous leaf imprints in the acid bath.

I love the zinc, I love the acid. I love the viscous printer's ink that I cannot remove from under my fingernails. I love the quiet, cool studio. I don't mind the little cuts and nicks on my fingers from the sharp metal edges. I don't mind that the cuts sting when I reach into the acid bath. I can't use the rubber gloves. They are clumsy and disrupt the rhythm of my work which carries me away like a meditation.

And when the image is complete, I print it for the first time; an artist's proof, a Jewish American girl's etching of a Mexican Catholic church in tones of ochre, indigo and terracotta. The title is "La Despedida." It is a sadly beautiful goodbye to Julio.

August 2009 Metepec, Estado de Mexico:

Nowadays people say "*gringa*" in my presence, but it's not referring to me. Taxi drivers ask how long I've lived in Mexico. Fifteen years, I answer and they say, "*Ud. es más de aquí que de allá.*" Am I more from here than there? A friend has said, "*Eres más mexicana que el nopal.*" "You are more Mexican than a nopal cactus." But I'm not. I am an American who has lived in Mexico for 15 years. I suspect that my heart is Mexican. I belong to both places just as I belong to neither.

I speak English. I speak Spanish. When speaking Spanish, I have been asked if I am Argentine, by a Mexican, or if I am Israeli, by a Colombian Jew. When speaking English, I have been asked how I learned English so well, by an American. English will always be my first language. I will always have an accent when speaking Spanish. I learned Spanish as a young adult, but, sometimes, according to my family in the U.S., my English is strange or stilted. The Spanish language has altered who I am as have all of my learning and experience.

My Jewishness lay dormant until my Mexican and American daughter ("More Mexican than American, Mom," she insists in English!) requested to prepare for her Bat Mitzvah. This was a couple of years ago when she was 11. So we joined the closest synagogue, in Mexico City, an hour away. My daughter's Catholic father drove her to Hebrew class twice a week for a year. She became a Bat Mitzvah in July and brought joy to me, to her grand-parents, to her great grandparents (in spirit) and to generations going back thousands of years.

We have a second home in San Miguel and try to spend as much time there as we can. The blind beggar is still there and he is the only one who hasn't aged. We visit family in the U.S. once or twice a year and they visit us. Julio and I remain friends. He is a permanent U.S. resident. His parents live in San Miguel. My daughter knows who she is. She belongs everywhere she goes.

Ellen Lurie graduated from Kenyon College with a B.A. in Fine Arts (concen-tration in printmaking). She received an M.S. in Social Work from Columbia University. She worked as a bilingual social worker in mental health clinics for children and families in New York City, as an adjunct professor in the clinical training of candidates for Master Degree in Social Work at Columbia University and New York University and as a bilingual social worker for the New York City Board of Education. She has lived in Mexico since 1994. She currently lives in Metepec, Estado de Méxcio with her daughter. Ellen co-founded Outsourcing English Services and teaches and implements English programs in companies in Toluca, Estado de México and surrounding industrial zones.

¿Agua?

Pam Quick

J had visited San Miguel many times although, at this point in history, I had no experience at house-sitting in Mexico. Nevertheless, I enthusiastically accepted a friend's offer to take care of her house on Zacateros for a week in April. I figured it would be similar to taking care of my own home. My friend mentioned gas and water delivery, but that didn't seem too hard. I was just beginning the Level I Warren Hardy Spanish class and eager to communicate with the Mexicans who were sharing their city with me. Deliverymen would be great opportunities.

One day, as I returned to the house from a sun-drenched trip to Espino's, I encountered an exhausted-looking young fellow on the sidewalk.

"*¿Agua?*" quietly asked the perspiring teenager leaning on the wall near the courtyard door. The sun was pounding down from high overhead, the time of day neither of us should have been walking around outside.

"Oh. *¡Sí! ¡Un momento!*" I cheerfully responded as I unlocked the door. "*Yo regreso en un momentito,*" I assured him with the joy of being able to quickly help a thirsty local.

As he stood there, looking at me with a blank stare (from dehydration, I presumed), I smiled and closed the door. I ran across the courtyard, dashed into the kitchen and filled a large glass with purified water from the big blue jug on the counter.

Back across the courtyard, I opened the door and stepped out onto the sizzling sidewalk to hand him the glass. He accepted the water tentatively, now looking genuinely puzzled. He held the glass without drinking.

Suddenly, his face took on an enormous grin. He took a sip. "*Gracias,*" he said, at this point virtually beaming. He took another grinning sip. He seemed so happy! I felt happy, too. I decided to try to chat a little. I began with my best weather statement, the one I had just practiced in the grocery store and on several taxi drivers. "*Hace mucho calor,*" I said, fanning my face for emphasis.

The sweating fellow took a long swallow and beamed another glorious smile. "*Sí, Señora,*" he agreed, nodding seriously. "*Hace mucho calor.*"

Then with a twinkle in his eye, he turned his gaze to the truck idling across the street, a Santorini delivery truck loaded with blue water jugs. Barely containing his laughter, the young man gestured toward the jug-filled truck with his half-filled glass before turning to ask, "*Necesita mas aqua hoy, Señora?*"

He waited the few seconds it took for me to catch up with the reality of the situation. Then we both broke into gales of laughter, along with the truck driver who had witnessed the whole event.

I bought two jugs which my strong, chuckling friend carried on his shoulders all the way to the kitchen counter, surely enjoying the funniest delivery of his day. I laughed again as I closed the gate behind Señor H$_2$O, wondering when a man needing gas would come knocking.

My parents brought me to Mexico for the first time in 1960, the beginning of my fifty-year love affair with this exhilarating, delicious country. The gentle smiling people and Mexico's joyful sensory overload have made me happily return many times as a visitor, and now my husband and I rent a small apartment in San Miguel de Allende as our second home. We live the rest of our time in another kind of beauty in the Ozark Mountains, in the little village of Eureka Springs, Arkansas. Like San Miguel, picturesque Eureka Springs is listed on its country's National Register of Historic Places. I write stories and take photographs to share cultural comparisons and insights from the creative inspiration of both of my hometowns.

Burdens

Susan Dorf

n the chill of the morning, a string of black Ibis wind their way across a rosy pink sky over the high desert plain. Under a scrawny mesquite tree by the reservoir, two men are scooping rich soil from the shore into flour sacks and loading them onto the backs of two waiting burros. The smells of animals and earth and wood smoke from the nearby village fill the air. They work silently, the burros shifting under the growing weight of their load, their ears twitching among the flies that buzz lazily around their heads.

Finally, the bags are tied onto the animals with rope, and men and beasts begin the long climb up the hillside toward the clanging church bells of San Miguel. They walk past the bright green alfalfa fields and the small adobe and brick houses, climbing over the railroad tracks by the old abandoned train station to where the dirt roads turn to pavement at the edge of town. They lead the animals uphill toward the center of town, passing children in school uniforms who are carrying day packs full of books, their hair slicked back and shoes freshly shined. They nod to the housewives and maids in aprons and rebozos carrying their plastic shopping bags down to the market. Gringos weave past them on the stone sidewalks carrying yoga mats, Spanish books, sketch pads and laptops. Early morning traffic grinds its way up the narrow streets.

A dusty golden light peeks over the tops of the buildings, slanting across the ochre and sienna walls and meandering up the cobblestone streets and into the courtyards and gardens as a new crescent moon fades into the lightening sky. The hot, yeasty fragrance from the local bakery mingles with the smell of diesel fumes and wet stones. Pigeons coo and flap from various niches in the old stone and brick buildings. Doorways open and young women with plastic buckets sprinkle water onto the dusty streets as if bestowing blessings.

The men lead their burros into the nicer neighborhoods at the top of the hill, wandering the streets from door to door and offering their bags of earth for sale as fertilizer for the gardens that lie hidden behind the high walls of the big houses. They wipe the sweat from their foreheads as they unload the bags, the shadows growing shorter as the sun rises higher in the sky.

By mid-afternoon, they pass by an outdoor café where tourists and locals are having lunch under colorful umbrellas. At one small table, a middle-aged couple sip lemonade, circling real estate ads in the local English language newspaper. Having recently sold their LA condo, they have come to seek refuge and a simpler life in Mexico, where they hope to buy a colonial house near the center of town. Already they have signed up for Spanish classes, joined a few local clubs and made several friends. They have fallen in love with the town and the people, surrounded by such heartbreaking beauty and are happy to have discovered this charming little place they are now calling their home.

The men stop to rest next to the café to water their animals at a fountain built into the side of a building. Two brown-skinned men in stained clothes and straw hats; two burros carrying mounds of white sacks, casting russet colored shadows against a *terra cotta* wall.

Across the street a man in khaki shorts, pale legs planted into white socks and sandals, canvas safari hat perched on his balding head, raises his Nikon to eye level, squinching up his face as he makes a few adjustments to the camera, zooming in on the men with the burros. He can't believe his luck. Last year, his picture of a beggar woman carrying a small child in a shawl had won him second prize in the county fair in his hometown. And now here is this perfectly quaint scene, presenting itself to him like a gift.

At the click of the shutter, the men with the burros jerk their heads up toward the sound. They watch intently as the man re-adjusts the camera for a second shot. If it seems strange to them that anyone would want to take their photograph, they don't let on. Instead, their faces take on a sudden look of desperation, and they thrust their empty hands out towards him.

The man with the camera blinks, as if surprised that the men are actually alive and not just figurines placed there for his personal viewing pleasure. What now? He tips his hat nervously, uncertain as to what to do next, uncomfortable that he has to acknowledge them. He begins to back away, the heavy black camera twisting awkwardly around his neck.

The couple at the table have looked up from their newspaper to witness the scene. They see the poor Mexicans with the overburdened burros. They see the clueless tourist with the enormous lens, lurking away. Suddenly they are both on their feet, the man pointing an accusing finger at the Nikon.

"Hey!" He shouts. "For chrissakes, give them a few pesos, why dontcha?" The man with the camera stops and turns to see where the voice is coming from.

"You can't just walk around taking pictures of people without their permission, you know," says the woman. She is standing with the newspaper clenched in her hand. Perhaps she plans to hit him with it. Instead, she shoves it into a shopping bag decorated with an image of the Virgin of Guadalupe and crosses her arms, glaring at him.

The man with the camera stares at them, then back to the Mexicans, who are still standing with their outstretched hands. Their desperate faces soften unwittingly into confused and mild amusement as they witness the drama unfolding before them. The man with the camera looks sheepish, as if he has been caught stealing. He tries to speak, but he can't imagine what he should say, and so begins to fumble awkwardly in his pockets.

Dark moons of sweat reveal themselves beneath the armpits of his Banana Republic shirt as coins tumble and clatter onto the cobblestones. He crouches down to gather them and stands and steadies himself, sees the two men talking softly to each other, nodding their chins toward him. He sees the American couple turn and walk away, shaking their heads. Then he moves slowly, nervously towards the men and drops a few coins into each of the earth-brown hands. He can smell the stench of the animals, the dust and the sweat. The men tip their hats and offer him their crinkled smiles. He nods his head and manages a nervous grin. The men pocket the coins, and then one of them holds out his hand again, his palm turned sideways. The man with the camera reaches out and shakes the calloused hand with his own sweaty one, takes a full breath, then turns and slowly walks away, down the winding narrow streets to the cool safety of his hotel.

The burros, their loads somewhat lighter now, gratefully lap up the cool water from the fountain, then stand still and silent in the narrow shade of the overhanging bougainvillea, momentarily protected from the heat of the afternoon sun. They close their eyes and rest. As far as they are concerned, this is as good as it gets.

Susan Dorf fell in love with Mexico in the 1970's when she first crossed the border with a backpack, despite (and most likely because of) all of the warnings of danger from family and friends. Instead, she found a land and culture that fed her soul and ignited her imagination. Having spent many years travelling and living in various parts of the country, she currently divides her time between San Miguel and the central coast of California. Primarily a visual artist, writing was her first love. She has had stories published in the Porter Gulch Review *as well as on her blog:* (http://artpilgrim3.blogspot.com) *and hopes to self publish a collection of her stories on Mexico in the near future. Susan is bi-lingual in Spanish and English. She can be reached at susan@susandorf.com*

A Neighbor's Concern

LAURA JULIET WOOD

I worry that Erika lives in a one-room, concrete *casita*
on the side of a steep set of stairs into town
and imagine that the house might slide down
our modest but crumbling mountain.

I watch her hang clothes up on the roof,
pot geraniums in empty cans of evaporated milk.
She shoulders her baby son under the pomegranate,
unaware of her own precarious tilt.

She's barely hanging on to that earth, no matter—
there are buildings below her and highways and trees
that would catch her before she disappeared.
The way I see it, the house is hinged on fate.

But at night Erika sits on her rooftop sipping a *cerveza*,
singing lullabies to her son and only sees, I now believe,
how the moonlight tips the earth toward her,
anchors her to the entrance of the world's gate.

Laura Juliet Wood graduated with an MFA in fiction from Columbia University in New York City. She first came to San Miguel from her hometown of Pensacola, Florida when she was nine years old, and has lived there permanently since 1999 where she teaches, edits and translates. In 2008, a workshop she took with poet Carolyn Forché inspired her to begin writing poetry again.

Bathed with Miracles and Magic

Leading an Enchanted Life in San Miguel de Allende

JOAL DONOVAN

J think of it as God's great gift. In 1971, the congregation of St. Paul's Anglican Church decided that they needed a full-time priest. Through a series of marvelous coincidences, my husband, John, was called to be their first rector. As the rector of St. Paul's in the Walls in Florence, Italy, said, when asked how he managed to get that plum assignment, "Jesus loves me." Indeed, I felt exactly the same: Jesus loved us.

We had vacationed twice in Mexico in the sixties; and John and I both had fallen in love with Mexico and all things Mexican. The opportunity to move to San Miguel was a "dream come true." My husband could actually work as an English speaking priest in this enchanted town, It was beyond my wildest yearnings, my most secret and hoped for imaginings. But it was true.

The moment we crossed the border, I knew that the experience would change all of us (sons Mark, eight; Harris, five; and Tom, one) forever. We were bombarded with loud music, hawkers selling their wares, houses painted the colors of watermelons and mangoes, people on the streets everywhere. This was a country where life was lived passionately and expansively.

Music was blaring as we drove through Nuevo Laredo, John was dodging taxis, bicycles, and vendors, and I was giving thanks block by colorful block for this "*gran aventura.*" *Gracias a Dios*, our lives were going to be *picante* and bright, no more drab pastels for *familia* Donovan!

The congregation had rented a house for us on Calle San Francisco; we had moved most of our furniture down. Surprisingly (I later came to know just how surprisingly), the furniture arrived three days after our arrival. In the meantime, we were given accommodations at the Hotel de las Monjas until the furniture arrived, and we were invited to breakfast, lunch, and dinner with various members of the congregation until we were settled.

People through the years have often asked me if being a minister's wife is difficult. Do the congregations expect too much of the minister's family? In our case, I have always found that being a minister's family is a huge PLUS. Wherever you go, you are immediately taken in and surrounded by a bigger family. You are accepted and loved before people even get to know you. It was certainly true moving to San Miguel and becoming part of St. Paul's family. People were accepting, welcoming, warm, and loving.

Most of the congregation was much older than our little family. They were retired couples who had moved here to enjoy and participate in this lovely, lively culture. But they seemed genuinely pleased to have a young family in their midst. Our children suddenly had a plethora of surrogate grandparents. And our presence also seemed to bring young families out of the woodwork.

It was toward the end of the hippie era. Quite a few younger families had come to San Miguel to get away from the "rat race," to live an alternate life style. And there were always young families who came on sabbaticals for "Papa" to write his novel, or compose a symphony, or paint. Some of these families found their way to St. Paul's and the church began to have a slightly younger profile.

San Miguel was far different in the 1970s than it is today. There were almost no restaurants. I can name them on one hand: La Bugambilia (at that time, it was under the *portales*), the Hotel San Francisco, the Hotel Atascadero, and Don Fenton opened a little hamburger joint called El Hambre. Barbara Dobarganes had a drugstore, La Botica, on Calle San Francisco, where you could get a milk shake and soda drinks. And there was La Llave, a kind of bar/restaurant across the street from the house the church later bought to be the rectory on Calle Aldama.

Life was simpler then. Not much traffic. Not many films. (Although the Cine Hermanos Aldama did show some Class B or C movies.) No Chamber Music Festivals. Very little at the Angela Peralta Theater, or anywhere else. *But*, we had Mexican festivals and fiestas. We had this rich culture, and that was enough.

The Playreaders of San Miguel was started shortly after we arrived. George and Lulu Massey, a couple who attended St. Paul's and who "just loved amateur theater," started the Playreaders. In the early days, the readings were held at the San Francisco Hotel with the readers sitting on stools. Then we started meeting in different venues: sometimes the theater at the Instituto, sometimes at the Bellas Artes. In time, the plays began to be staged.

John and I were both active in the Playreaders, John as an actor, and I liked both acting and directing. I directed "A Man for All Seasons" on stage at Bellas Artes. This was a fully staged production, but the actors did carry their scripts. We had had about four rehearsals with only a couple of rehearsals left, when the young woman playing Thomas More's daughter told me that she had been invited to a wedding and could she get a replacement. I wasn't thrilled with the idea, but I told her that, if she found someone, and I could talk to her and felt okay about it, then she could.

The next morning the doorbell rang and it was a young woman named Deborah. She wanted to know if she could read Susan's part. Deborah was blind. I could not imagine how she would find a braille script. I was less than enthusiastic and I told her that I thought it would be very difficult (if not impossible) for her to learn the stage directions at this late date, plus, did she happen to have a braille script? She told me that she did not, but that she could transcribe it into braille if someone would read the script to her. Could I do it?

I told her I could not. I was presently trying to get my children off to school and I had other commitments until our 1:00 rehearsal. She asked if she could come to the rehearsal if she found someone to read the script to her before then. I reluctantly agreed. In fact, my heart sank. How on earth was this going to work?

That afternoon, Deborah was at the theater with script in hand, and read she did. She was actually quite good. With the help of other cast members, she managed her entrances, exits and movement on stage. When we gave the performance, a hush fell over the audience as they began to detect that one reader was reading her script with her fingers, not her eyes. I will never quite be able to express the willingness and eagerness with which the audience participated in this amazing experience. It was as though Deborah's blindness had opened *our* eyes. She was as capable, as moving, as participatory in every way as the other members of the cast. Perhaps it was mostly my own shortcomings that had imagined she would have trouble doing her part. She not only proved me wrong, she gave the whole cast a sense of community and camaraderie that they had not had before this.

When I collected their scripts at the end of the show, I went through them to see what kind of notes they had made for themselves. I noticed again and again that cast members had made notes to help Deborah. "Help Deb with her entrance here," "Squeeze Deb's hand" (before King Henry made his entrance, so she would know to bow) and "Lead Deb offstage as I exit." Deborah's participation had created an ensemble, a kind of miracle play.

John and I were part of the founding board of the José Vasconcelos School. Our eldest son, Mark, made the bus trek to the John F. Kennedy School in the Jurica, outside Querétaro. Two bus loads of students went there every day, 60 to 65 of them. It was the only bi-lingual school in these parts. Harris, our middle son, went to a kindergarten in town that was sponsored by the Kennedy School. It wasn't very organized, and, in fact, it left a great deal to be desired.

We, along with other friends, felt that we desperately needed a bilingual school in San Miguel. The parents involved were Tom and Madeline Horn, Sandy Gerez (later Cassandra Webb), Don Fenton, Hib and Gretchen Sabin, Bill Stark, and John and me. Non-parents were Estelle Clapp and Toni de Gerez, two women who were interested in education. We learned a lot more than we wanted to learn about starting a school in Mexico. It was an exhausting, frustrating, occasionally exhilarating, and finally, satisfying experience. I would *never* do it again, but we hung in together and we pulled it off.

The school opened in the fall of 1974 in a building on Calle Juarez. We had kinder through 4th grade. When our youngest son, Tom, went there for kindergarten in the fall of 1975, it had become a Montessori School. I will never forget the day Tom came home from school to announce that they were going to do a play, "Goldilocks," and that he had a really big part.

When I asked him which of the bears he was playing, he indignantly told me that he was going to be Goldilocks! (He was the only one in the class with golden "locks.")

Our days in San Miguel were filled to the brim with children, with church, theater, starting a school, but, perhaps, they are most memorable for the nights we would wake our children up in the middle of the night to walk to the *jardín* in the brisk night air to watch fireworks. I have rich memories of many family hikes in the canyons on either side of town, walking through the dry river beds, coming upon small pools and an occasional waterfall. I can still feel my little children's hands in mine as we walked through the dark tunnel into the crater we discovered close to Valle de Santiago.

Our family delights in remembering our "journey to Xichu," when we had two flat tires, found ourselves driving through a cornfield, were caught in a hailstorm and discovered that our windshield wipers didn't work...all in all, a perfect day. My heart still skips beats when I think, again, of our little three year old, Tom, doing the Dance of the Viejito at a *hacienda* party. And I am often overcome with nostalgia and longing as I recall walking behind the Estudiantinas one night when the lights went out and block after block, San Miguelenses came onto their balconies holding burning candles.

The five years we lived in this Mexican hill town were years of new experiences, new smells, new tastes, new sounds: the bells pealing, the dogs barking, the castillos whistling, the bottle rockets exploding, the mariachis playing. Supper at our house was almost always warm tortillas with leftovers, beans, or avocados rolled up inside. Our kitchen without mangoes was like a day without sunshine. They were delicious years of wonder and delight.

The sensory experience of those years, the friendship and warmth of St. Paul's family, the field trips we made with Lupe Saucedo, the bishop (a small, gentle Tarascan Indian) to visit tiny Mexican Episcopal churches in the state of Hidalgo, the fireworks (ALWAYS the fireworks). I became something of a pyromaniac after living in Mexico. How does one celebrate without fireworks? And, finally, the lively, always friendly Mexican community. We were bathed with miracles and magic.

And, of course, the *jardín*: the living room of the town, welcoming one and all. We would take young Tom's tricycle down there in the late afternoons and, as he rode around, we would watch the world go by, visit with friends, listen to the mellifluous song of Spanish being spoken, speak Spanish ourselves (part of the charm of this people is their language). The bells would peal, the evening would fall, we would start our walk home. I don't remember whether we actually ate *paletas de guayaba* as we strolled home, or whether it is simply my memories that taste so delectable and sweet. It was an enchanted life.

Joal Donovan, a sometimes writer of poetry, essays, and memoir, uses her pen primarily to celebrate life, family, and friendships. Joal and husband John first came to San Miguel in 1969, then lived here for five years in the early '70s. For the last 15 years they have spent three plus months a year in this place and with these people. In another life, Joal, with her longtime friend, Sally Wallace, ran Hendley Market, a shop on Galveston's Strand. They carried folk art, antiques, nativities from every corner of the globe, and curious toys. Joal and John have three sons, Mark, Harris, and Tom. The abuelitos have five "grands." Her cup runneth over.

Writer in Exile

JON LOONEY

No one ever told me
That, as an ex-pat writer,
I would be washing dishes
Several times daily,
And — by hand.
Somehow,
That was not part
Of my dream
About living and writing
In another country.

In 1920's Paris,
Did Hemingway
Have to do
The breakfast dishes
And warm the baby formula for son Bumby
Before Hadley would
Let him run off
To his studio to write?

Did Zelda
Hound Scott
Until he relented
And hung their garbage

From a tree limb
To be taken away,
Just as I do In San Miguel?

In anything-goes Tangier,
Did Paul Bowles and Truman Capote
Have to do the day's shopping
And polish the silver for Jane
Before they withdrew
To their carpet-strewn rooms
To write?

Did Anais Nin, Isak Dinesen, and Beryl Markham
Ever have help with household duties?
In exile,
Did they manage
All the cooking and cleaning
Along with metaphors
And book contracts?

Who could have anticipated
That my artist's
Window on the world
Here,
In exotic San Miguel,
Would be the window
Above my kitchen sink!
Here, at my usual station,
I am not opposed to be turning a phrase or two
As I twist a soapy sponge
Into the throat of a glass.

But who would have thought
That washing bread crumbs
And tea stains
From ceramic ware

From Santa Rosa
And Dolores Hidalgo
Would have its creative aspect —
Turning lead-free ceramics
Into golden creations.

Certain days,
When the afternoon sun
Rinses through the window
Above the sink
Catching my newly completed work
Just-so, I see
Not dishes, but semi-precious jewels
Filling my drain board.

In my cool but literary house
Steam rises from the newly washed dishes.
An idea begins to form.

Jon Looney is the author of three volumes of poems: Uphill, Headwaters *and* Bluffwalker, Snakedoctor, Whistlepig. *His work is included in a number of anthologies including* Ozark, Ozark: A Hillside Reader, Ozarks Panorama, A Rough Sort of Beauty, *and* Solamente in San Miguel: Writings from the Authors' Sala of San Miguel de Allende. *His articles on American art have appeared in the* Journal of the Print World. *Jon divides his time between San Miguel and Colorado.*

Awakened on the Day of the Dead

GAIL YATES TOBEY

*L*ong before dawn on the Day of the Dead, I entered though heavy iron gates into the San Juan de Dios Cemetery. Cassie, my 18-year-old niece, followed close behind me. Moonlight made faint shadows on the gravel walkway; our footsteps crunched on fallen autumn leaves. The narrow beams of our flashlights hit the stone walls of the ancient graveyard, then moved on and reflected the glimmer of aged marble tombs. We walked into a small town of the dead.

Cassie and I have only been together for a few days. I had hoped to reestablish our close relationship that had been strained by the long illness and subsequent death of her mother. Two years ago, knowing her time was short, my beloved Sarah begged me to stay close to Cassie, her only child. I swore I would. However, since Sarah's funeral, Cassie had rejected my attempts to spend one-on-one time with her. I'd only seen her at occasional family get-togethers.

I was surprised when she accepted my invitation to go to Mexico with me. I don't know what she expected — maybe a beach resort with hot and cold running Latin lovers — but I'd brought her to my favorite Mexican town, San Miguel de Allende, a place high in the mountains and far from any ocean.

The first morning in San Miguel, we ate breakfast at an outdoor café on the *jardín*. While taking tentative bites of her *huevos rancheros,* Cassie read the latest issue of *People* magazine with its up-to-date reports on the lives of Paris Hilton and Britney Spears. In her personal grooming, I see their influence. Her blond hair is straight and long; she has butterfly-shaped, jeweled hair clips holding her bangs back. Her bright pink fingernails have acrylic tips with star designs and, arrayed halfway up her tanned arms, are silver bangles and charm bracelets.

In spite of my advice about the importance of modesty in Mexico, her white linen blouse reveals a broad width of midriff and her hip-hugger jeans look painted on. Striking blue eyes are visible through the pink lenses of her oversized, rhinestone-covered sunglasses. Her eyes are the color of my sister's and are ringed in a glittery violet eyeliner and eye shadow. In a concession to safe transit on the cobblestone streets, she wears Converse sneakers, veneered in ruby red sequins and laced-up over her ankles.

The next day, I took her on a shopping trip at the local artisans' *mercado*. Cassie chose a king's ransom of ornate necklaces, bracelets, and rings. She selected elaborate pewter fruit bowls for her grandparents, an embossed leather wallet for her father and hand-embroidered shawls for her two roommates. As I paid the bills, her brilliant teeth flashed between scarlet-painted lips. She looked happy for the first time since she arrived, but I felt frustrated that she didn't even say "thank you" to me. I was on the verge of crying. This is not at all like being on a trip with her mother — trips I fondly remembered. I began to regret my promise to Sarah.

Later in the week, after dragging Cassie to art galleries, churches, and abandoned silver mines, I arranged for us to go on a guided horseback trip into a nearby canyon. After riding our horses for several hours down into dry ravines and up slick, rock-covered slopes, we stopped under sheltering mesquite trees to eat a lunch of tamales, steamed in corn husks, and cactus salad. Both of us were hungry so Cassie deigned to eat some of the food she called "foreign." Across the valley, the dazzling sun began to descend behind the ruins of an ancient Otomi pyramid, built by the people who first settled these central Mexican highlands.

I relayed to Cassie the history of the pyramid and its people, but she expressed no interest. I began to think that my attempts at intimacy were hopeless. Maybe I would never again know Cassie's love for her "Auntie LaLa," her childhood name for me.

"Isn't that sunset beautiful?" I asked with resignation.

"Yeah, I guess. My butt's sore from that saddle. Can't we go back to town now? You promised we'd cruise the local discos."

So that's what we did. We returned to town and cruised the discos. We both drank copious amounts of tequila, straight up and in margaritas, until early in the morning. Cassie's not yet of drinking age in the U.S., but she's allowed to drink here and she held her own. I could barely keep up. She finally looked like she was enjoying herself as she swayed to the mariachi music. Young Mexican men, seeing her sparkling face and curvaceous body, approached to ask her to dance and when she agreed to do so, I kept a very close eye on her. At three in the morning, we left our last disco. Holding on to each other, almost like sisters, we wove down the streets to our B&B and, after splashing our faces with cold water, slipped into our beds surrounded by vivid Mexican paintings.

The morning of the 31st of October arrives. We only have a couple more days together. While Cassie and I nurse our hangovers by sipping cappuccinos in our room, I scan the *Atención*, the local weekly newspaper, and read about a special cemetery in town.

"Cassie, there's a cemetery here in town that's only open to the public one day a year, on the Day of the Dead. Let's visit it tonight, after midnight."

"Whatever," she says, looking up at me with a bored, blank stare.

Did I hear her correctly — she's willing to visit a cemetery after midnight?

Cassie puts the buds of her ever-present iPod into her ears and turns her head back down to *Entertainment Today*. She's catching up on what's happened in the lives of Hilton and Spears over the past twenty-four hours.

That evening we go to bed early. At 12:30 a.m., the alarm buzzes. I awaken Cassie from her sleep and we both dress in jeans and jackets as the night is chilly. From my nightstand, I grab a couple of flashlights.

A cab takes us to a quiet, poorly-illuminated section of town. The road is nearly empty. Using our flashlights, we walk along until we find the iron gate of the cemetery, heavily ornamented with angels and crosses. The gate is slightly ajar, but it's difficult to push open. Cassie doesn't help me. The rusted hinges give out a loud groan. For some reason, Cassie shushes me. As if there is anyone around here to wake up, I think.

Once through the gates, we walk on leaves that lay in piles beneath our feet. The crunch of the leaves is softer than on the street. The pungent scent of marigolds reaches my nostrils. We're walking on thousands of marigold pedals that are strewn throughout the graveyard. They guide us down the paths among the stone and marble tombs.

In spite of the hour, the cemetery is humming with life. There are dozens of small groups of people swarming around the graveyard, decorating the marble tombs and earthen graves. Everywhere I look, there are candy flowers, sugar cane arches, and flowers that ornament the tombs and graves. Many of decorations are lavish, overflowing with candy, baked rolls, fresh fruits, and drinks — cans of Coca Cola, shot glasses of tequila, and margaritas with slices of lime. On some of the grave sites, there are candies in the shape of skeletons, coffins, and human skulls. Most of the skulls have the names of loved ones written in script on their foreheads. Other candies are shaped like whiskey bottles, cigar and cigarette packs, and enticing desserts — ice cream sundaes, fruit pies, and slices of chocolate cake. The unmarked earthen graves are decorated with more simple adornments, often bearing only one or two brightly-lit candles stamped with images of the Virgin of Guadalupe.

"Ugh," Cassie says. She's right behind me and bumps into me. I turn around. She's grimacing and her eyes are thin slits. "I don't like this," she says.

"Oh, come on. There's nothing here that can hurt you," I say.

We walk further into the burial ground that holds the remains of generations of the deceased of San Miguel. Sleeping infants are lying on coverlets next to some of the graves. Toddlers are boldly making their way around the tombs in the semi-darkness, holding onto the hands of a parent or older sibling. Boys and girls are scattered around the graveyard, the younger ones chasing each other or throwing balls to their pet dogs, the older teens flirting or hugging in dark corners. Family groups are sitting on blankets beside many of the memorials, eating, drinking, talking, quietly singing, sometimes accompanied by a guitar, as if they were at a picnic in the park.

Cassie, silent, moves next to me. I wonder what she's thinking. Then I feel her tug on the sleeve of my denim jacket. She whispers, "Aunt Laura, this is morbid."

When I look, her face is drained of its usual pinkness and there is a strong frown line between her eyes, reminiscent of her mother when she was worried or in pain. This is the first strong reaction of any type that Cassie has shown during our time together.

I realize that, in our U.S. culture, we relate to death in a very different way from what we see here. The candy skeletons, skulls, and coffins can be disturbing to those who are unaccustomed to them.

"I'd hoped you'd find it interesting," I say, feeling downcast by Cassie's reaction. The strong presence of daily life, and its ordinary activity, in a place memorializing those who have died fascinates me. It's comforting to me. There doesn't seem to be sorrow here, only celebration. Even though I'm reluctant to leave, I ask her, "Do you want to leave?"

"Yeah, can we go now?" Cassie asks.

I continue to look at the family groups who are so peaceful and so much alive in the small town of the dead. Cassie tugs at my sleeve again.

"Aunt Laura, I want to go, now," she says. Her voice is tearful. We walk in silence back to the cemetery gate and find a taxi home.

From a guest bar in the B&B, I grab a couple of glasses and a bottle of tequila to take to our suite. Cassie plops down on the settee. Her face is turned away from me. I pour two fingers of tequila into two old fashion glasses.

"Here's something to make you feel better."

She turns towards me and takes the glass.

"You've been crying," I say. Tears have left channels in her make-up; her eyes look like Tammy Faye Baker's. "What has upset you?"

"I don't like seeing people celebrating death," she says.

"Oh." I don't know what else to say.

"It looks like they're mocking death. It's not something to play around with, you know. Death takes things away from you."

She begins sobbing. I move beside her and put my arms around her. She pushes me away. "I don't want you. I want her."

"I know."

Cassie glares at me with loathing. "Why couldn't you have died instead?" She grabs her glass from the coffee table and takes a big gulp, then another.

I gasp. A slap couldn't have been more shocking to me. I feel completely vulnerable to her outburst.

"When mom was ill, you were always there, but you weren't sick like mom — you were well."

I'm silent. What can I say?

"She was sick for so long. I was little, only eleven. I needed her."

"I know," my voice is weak with apprehension. What else is she going to say?

"No one needed you. You didn't even have a pet cat to take care of," Cassie says with anger.

I feel like I've been struck, but I labor hard to understand her. "Yes, it was unfair. Sometimes, I prayed that I'd be taken instead."

"Well, your prayers weren't answered."

"Cassie, I didn't know you felt this way."

She's silent. I look over at her. Her anger has hissed away. She looks deflated.

"I loved your mom, too. I really miss her too." My eyes well up with tears.

She looks me in the eyes and says with a softer tone, "I know that. I guess I didn't really want you to die. But how could she leave me?"

"She didn't want to leave. She wanted to be with you while you grew up. She wanted to be at your graduations, your wedding, at the births of your children. She wanted to be there for you." .

Cassie doesn't respond. Tears have smeared the violet eyeliner down her cheeks. The jeweled clips have fallen out of her hair and her bangs hang limp over her forehead.

I go on, "Those letters she wrote you — for you to open on those special times in your life. She wrote the letters because she wanted you to know that with all her heart she wished to be with you."

"But she left me," Cassie says. She turns her head toward the back of the sofa. Her sobs are softer, but her body still quivers.

I touch her back and then rub it. She doesn't shake me off. I have nothing more to say that can help Cassie because of my belief that when people die, they are gone. Their body deteriorates and eventually goes back to the elements. Dust to dust. I don't believe in Heaven or Hell, and don't believe there is anything like a soul. Survivors carry the memory of their loved ones in their hearts, but their actual presence is no longer a part of their life. With my view of death, there is nothing comforting that I can say to Cassie.

We sit together on the sofa, my arm around her shoulders, silent, for hours.

As I sit there with Cassie, thoughts and images rush through my head: Sarah's wonderful laugh, the trips we took to Spain, Italy and Mexico, remembering how together we cried all night when she told me that the breast cancer had spread. I felt again the devastation that had I felt when all hope was lost.

It's too painful for me to dwell on any longer. Shaking my head, I pursue another line of thought. What are other ways of thinking about death? Does death always need to be the end? What was the meaning of the events in the cemetery earlier this morning?

Cassie's breath is obstructed as it moves in and out of her nose and she begins to snore. As I leave the sofa, I let her body slide into a comfortable position. I've had too much tequila, but I'm relieved that Cassie has let me hold her. Asleep, she reminds me so much of Sarah.

The *Atención* is still on the floor. I search through the pages until I find the article about the San Juan de Dios cemetery. I read about the Day of the Dead. I learn that there *is* meaning in the traditions — decorating the graves, providing candy replicas of their loved one's favorite things, and making personal altars. In Mexico, there's a blend of Aztec and Catholic beliefs; they believe that death is a part of life. It does not end life, but is merely a transition from one stage to another. With their rituals, throwing brightly colored, pungent marigold petals to guide the spirits home; making personal altars in their homes; and decorating the graves and tombs, they believe that, one day a year, survivors can call back the departed spirits. They can nourish and revitalize them with candy symbolizing the things they had loved in life. Death does not separate you from the ones you love. You can always have them with you and, at least once a year, you can have a major celebration with them.

When Cassie awakens, I'll apologize to her for not recognizing her pain earlier. I'll tell her what I've learned about the Day of the Dead — how her mom hasn't left us after all. Then, on this day, our last day in San Miguel, I'll ask Cassie to help me collect candy replicas of the things Sarah loved, and create a personal altar to her mom, to my sister.

Gail Yates Tobey, Ph.D. is a freelance author and photographer who made San Miguel de Allende her home three years ago. Born in Virginia, she studied nursing and psychology at UVA and Penn. She was a professor at Penn and at Rutgers University, and practiced as a clinical psychologist in Chestertown, Maryland. She has published research articles and fiction and non-fiction pieces in the on-line journals Six Word Memoirs *and* Field Reports. *She has been a member of writers' groups in Philadelphia and in San Miguel. She especially appreciated the help of the San Miguel group.* Awakened on the Day of the Dead *is a fictional-ized work in memory of her younger sister, Sharon, who died of cancer. She is currently working on a novel based on an spine-tingling sailing trip she took from the mangrove swamps of Belize to the Chesapeake Bay.*

Thoroughly Modern Lucha

Dianne Walta Hart

"Great legs," Lucha heard someone say as she headed toward an SUV parked on the dusty school grounds. Lucha laughed in such a way that it was almost an admission that she'd heard it all before.

Lucha, decked out in a maroon top, black skirt, and black high heels, looks like a thoroughly modern woman. She's a fifty-year-old elementary school teacher, wife of a teacher, and mother of three sons, one of whom has studied in London. She's a school principal who had just organized a program where her students performed dance routines. Afterward, the guests — the district administrator and dozens of foreigners — feasted on food made by her students' parents. María de la Luz Jiménez Rodríguez, otherwise known as Lucha, was feeling unabashedly good and a compliment about her legs, well, that was gravy.

What distinguishes Lucha from smart hard-working professional women everywhere is that she accomplishes all this in Los Ricos de Abajo, a village across the Río Laja perched on a high desert plateau about a half-hour from San Miguel de Allende.

In 1990, the residents of Los Ricos decided that it was time for their children to receive their elementary school education in the *rancho*. They pooled together *ejido* land and manual labor; then they solicited help from the monks at the nearby Monasterio Nuestra Senora de la Soledad. The monks raised funds from Mexico, Canada, and the United States. As a result, the people of Los Ricos named their school Naciones Unidas.

Next step: hire a teacher. That was Lucha.

But how to get there? It's hard to reach. Lucha took the bus from her home in San Miguel to the Pemex station on the road to Dolores Hidalgo and then walked for an hour. Once in Los Ricos, the trip didn't get easier. A walk farther up the hill was required to get to the school. The school sat on a hilltop with a 360-degree view of the countryside. Beautiful, but remote.

Lucia was thirty years old, married with children. She had just earned her Licenciatura in Education from the Universidad Pedagógica Nacional in Guanajuato. She asked herself, "What in the world am I doing here?"

It soon would be Lucha's school, but had someone told her then that, twenty years later, she'd still be there, she would have shaken her head and said, "Not a chance." The school district told her she would have to stay only three years, but as it turned out, when that time was up, she was hooked.

Occasionally, a fellow teacher was able to give Lucha a ride, but, for most of these years, she made the long walk with a *machete* in her hand, looking over her shoulder for packs of wild dogs that prey on people walking. She now uses the six-year-old pedestrian bridge to cross the Laja, but one year the river washed out the bridge, forcing her to go across in a shaky version of a high-wire act.

Over time, she has come to know everyone in Los Ricos, how they're related to each other, the good they've done, and the terrible. Lucha says, "Every student has a story," and she keeps their stories in mind as she teaches them.

People in Los Ricos survive however they can: working in the cornfields, making tortillas, toiling in the nearby brick factory, selling snacks in the yard of the Atotonilco church, or going to San Miguel to clean houses or to play guitar on the street. Some people go to Mexico City, but others head toward the U.S. Lucha estimates that only 10 percent of the parents are gone at any given time. Most stay and work, one foot ahead of the other, and hope for a better life for their children.

This starts with the school. Eventually, another classroom and a kinder-garten were added to the hilltop site. The parents built a playground, a fence, and latrines. Lucha planted poinsettias.

In 2004, encouraged by donors and Lucha, Feed the Hungry, a San Miguel charitable organization that feeds 4,000 children every school day, started looking at Los Ricos. The problems were that Los Ricos did not have enough students to fit their guidelines and it was on the wrong side of the river, making it difficult to find a volunteer to deliver weekly groceries. But Los Ricos is *so* poor, Lucha told them. Eventually, Feed the Hungry constructed a kitchen and hired two local cooks, and volunteers signed up to get the food to the school. In January, 2005, the first meal was served to the children.

A year later, again with Lucha's leadership and donor funds, after-school English classes began, and residents could hear the Hokey Pokey coming from every room on the hilltop. Before long, the same volunteers began a small library, stuffing books into baggies once a week for Lucha's students to borrow.

When Lucha started teaching, few parents could read and write. Now their children are finishing elementary school. School costs money in Mexico: the school assessment, uniforms, school supplies often add up to a sum that Los Ricos parents can't afford. As a result, for many years, the sixth grade signaled the end of their children's education.

Today, however, Lucha's students who graduate from the sixth grade are continuing their educations by attending Atotonilco's *telesecundaria* with scholarships funded by donors and her school's volunteer English teachers and managed by Lucha.

Traditionally, few Los Ricos students continued their education after the 9th grade because most needed to find employment to help their families. Lucha has started talking to her students while they are still under her guidance, trying to instill goals and encouraging them to think about their futures. They appear to have listened. Many are going on to high school — with scholarships — and are now talking about studying medicine, law, teaching, architecture, and gastronomy.

Her students recognize the force of Lucha. One student, now in the ninth grade, said, "The reason children from Los Ricos do so well in secondary school is that they really *teach* us." And, to the pride of everyone involved, the principal of the Atotonilco's secondary school says that Los Ricos students come better prepared than students from other *ranchos*.

A smile is always on Lucha's face, whether she's comforting a child who has fallen or explaining the intricacies of Mexican bureaucracy. She's so short that some of her students loom over her, but she's a common-sense woman and bearer of definite decisions so that none of the students, not even the tall ones, would ever think of challenging her.

Although Los Ricos remains one of the poorest *ranchos*, Lucha notes how the houses have improved over the years. The school, too, has improved. It now has toilets (the only flush toilets in Los Ricos). They are kept clean by squads of Lucha's students wielding mops. Lucha now says, "Other schools want what Los Ricos has."

No matter where she is, on a hill top or in a classroom, Lucha's accomplishments demonstrate that she is indeed a thoroughly modern woman. Great legs and all.

Dianne Walta Hart first came to San Miguel in 1992 to visit a friend, returned every year after that, and, since 2001, she and her husband, Tom, have been homeowners and part-time residents. She taught in the Los Angeles Unified School District and at Oregon State University in Corvallis where she directed a study-abroad program in Ecuador and OSU's International Degree. She also served as the Latin America Director of the Oregon University system's international internship program and, in 2005, taught Migrant Studies at UNLA in Morelia. She is the author of two books: Thanks to God and the Revolution: The Oral History of a Nicaraguan Family *and* Undocumented in L.A.: An Immigrant's Story.

The Proposal

Margaret Tallis

After seven years, I was finished with my work at the stable training potential championship horses and their riders. I was tired
of the grueling hard work in the sun, and was now studying
massage therapy. At that time, one had to have a sponsor or
employer in order to get working papers in Mexico. I didn't have a sponsor — an employer — and it didn't seem likely I would get one, yet I had
to work.

I asked Javier, "What should I do?"

"We'll go to the Immigration Office and talk to them, he said. "I know
people who work there."

The federal government office, Migración, was at the edge of San Miguel's
Benito Juarez Park next to the Villa Santa Monica Hotel. This park was once
known to the locals as the French Park, I suppose, because of its layout:
dirt paths criss-crossed throughout, with benches strategically placed below
a green canopy of large trees. There were no grassy areas, but broad-leafed
plants tall and thick filled in geometric spaces. It was a cool, fresh refuge,
especially during the hot months of April and May. Egrets nested there. I
could hear them squawking as we got out of the car.

As we walked through the old plastered doorway of the Migración office,
we were met with the odors of paper and perfume. The clacking of type-
writer keys was sporadic, starting and stopping, with an occasional DING.
We stationed ourselves at the antique wooden counter. Files and boxes were
stacked up around the walls of this large room, and doors led to outer offices.
A row of desks faced each other in the middle of the room.

We stationed ourselves at the antique wooden counter. An official carrying a stack of papers walked in through one of the doors. He dropped them on a desk. This was The Man. He who, by the grace of God, lets you stay in Mexico. We caught his eye as he scanned the room and, hoping to draw his attention, we quickly said *"Buenas tardes,"* as if we were saluting a General. The official nodded his head toward us as he gave instructions to a woman who was filing her nails, and then he disappeared through a door, his attention firmly averted from us. The woman sighed at the interruption to her manicure, looked at the papers casually, then headed for the bathroom. Workers from the back offices came in the room, shuffled papers, opened and closed files. Papers were stamped, one after another, a rhythmic sound like a hammer hitting a nail. All typewriters were engaged in a symphony of dinging sounds punctuated by the occasional ringing of a telephone.

We waited. We waited. We waited. If we had been in a restaurant, we could have made the familiar shsss sound to get the waiter's attention. Not here. Strict manners were required This office decreed whether or not one would get those sacred papers. Humbleness, politeness, best Spanish, psychological preparedness, staying focused on what was wanted had to be the approach. We had dressed in our best, formal clothes. We both wore black pants. He wore a white shirt and tie. I wore a silk pink blouse, jewelry and make up. Our concert clothes.

A woman typed with long, long nails. How could she hit the keys without breaking one or, worse, chipping the nail polish? I wondered. She stopped, reached for her purse and pulled out a powder compact. She opened it, held it close to her face, moved the small mirror around, inspected every millimeter. With her finger, she wiped smudged mascara from under her eye. She snapped the compact closed, returned it to her purse, inspected her hands and nails, then turned to another typist who stopped punching keys, eager to engage in conversation. Ten minutes of boyfriend updates. Javier was beginning to get impatient. I was listening to the gossip. The woman finally noticed us. She continued to talk with her friend, looking back over her shoulder as she moved away from her desk.

Her perfume preceded her as she stepped toward us and looked at both of us. We chimed *"Buenas tardes"* like baby birds ready to receive a worm. *"Buenas tardes,"* she said. She directed a courteous smile at me which implied,

I see you standing there, but I'm going to speak to him. Yeah, I thought, don't speak to me. I'm just a woman...like you.

"*Soy Señorita America,* how can I help you", she said.

Señorita America. I looked at Javier, saw him slide his eyes toward me with that little glance that almost always made me laugh and I shifted my gaze and stared straight ahead to keep from blowing it.

Miss America! There she stood with her high gloss red nails, her stiletto heels, her tight black short skirt, her white blouse unbuttoned to the bra, and oh yes, her wet red high gloss, best-of-Joan-Crawford lips. That her eyelashes didn't get entangled from gobs of mascara was a mystery to me. Every hair was in place on that fantastic head in a sexy, shiny cascade of black curls.

Javier's grin almost ran off his face as he spoke to her. A long, drawn out discussion, the result being that the only way I could stay, and work, in the country was if Javier and I got married. Javier shifted nervously on his feet. I looked seriously into Javier's eyes. "Or I will have to go back to Canada. That's it. I'll have to go back."

The typewriters stilled. The workers stood up. The nail filing stopped. The room was silent. I stood looking at Javier. Silence. Seconds passed. Silence. Beads of sweat formed on his forehead.

He smiled, "Well, we'll get married, yes, let's get married".

Silence. JOY hit me in the stomach. I thought of the time we went to Javier's mother's ranch on the road to Dolores Hidalgo, a few miles outside of San Miguel, a year after we had met, a family fiesta. *El tío* José was there, the oldest brother of Javier's mother, Doña Gloria. José was the patron of the extended family. José's wife and children were there, too

José looked more indigenous than Spanish, short, dark, a little overweight. He spoke with confidence. His manners reflected his authority to represent the family. He was clearly in charge that day.

Before we arrived, the long table had been set up in the dusty yard under a canvas tarp for shade — a grudging sign of respect from Javier's mother. An embroidered tablecloth with glass dishes I had never seen before at Doña Gloria's house, were properly set out. She had clearly been ordered to keep the plastic dishes out of sight.

I was told to sit at the end of the table. José sat to my right. After small talk about the family, he leaned toward me and said, "You are the one he has chosen."

Doña Gloria was setting the chicken mole and rice on the table, but, at José's announcement, she inclined her head toward me and said, "She doesn't even speak Spanish."

I looked anxiously at Javier. Are you going to defend me, I thought.

Javier answered, "But she understands it, *madre*."

And I understood, too, that this was a kind of ritual, a ritual of approval and acceptance into the family. This was a decision made by the men, at the convenience and judgment of only the men, and Javier's mother had no choice but to participate. I felt important, strong and cared for, in spite of Doña Gloria's comments. I had been accepted by the men, and that was what was important on that day those several years ago.

So here I was now, in the Migración office, getting the marriage proposal I'd never especially thought about, or ever thought would come. I looked at Javier as we stood facing each other in that office. He had that happy expression on his face, the one where he was about to break out in song. He loved to sing those beautiful classic Mexican ballads and he sang to me often, my favorite: "La Paloma."

"*Si a tú ventana llega una paloma, trátala con cariño que es mi persona...*"

"If a dove arrives at your window, treat it with love, because it is me..."

I hadn't imagined myself as a married woman even though, since we had lived together for over six years, we were considered married by common law. I was forty one years old. He was seven years younger. Neither of us had been married before. Javier's uncle Hector, I thought, could finally look me the eyes instead of glancing away whenever we met. I would be respectable and yes, Javier was the only man I had ever loved.

Silence. Javier stood self conscious, still smiling, his face turning red.

The whole office waited for the answer. I took a deep breath. Suddenly, I blurted out, "Does this mean I can cook Mexican food?" Earlier he had told me Mexican women don't get married until they can cook.

He laughed. "Yes, you cook good Mexican food."

I sighed in relief. "Well," I said, "let's get married."

"*Sí!*" The people in the room said the word for me. Clapping, clapping for five minutes and more! People standing behind us, waiting their turn, exclaimed hearty "Congratulations" in English and shook our hands.

Chatter and laughter and happiness throughout the office: Our faces open books of embarrassment at what we had just done...in public.

Margaret Tallis was born in Saskatoon, Sask. Canada. She received a Bachelor of Fine Arts from the University of Saskatchewan in 1977 where she studied painting, drawing and printmaking. She has exhibited her work in Canada and Mexico. Margaret was involved in the equestrian business for over 35 years and competed successfully in Canada, the United States and Mexico. In 1986, she moved to San Miguel. In 1991, she studied "Touch For Health." Later, Margaret studied Reiki, Jin Shin, Jyutsu and, more recently, with the Asclepius Foundation. She is presently a practicing massage therapist. She began her writing career in 2000. The Proposal *is part of a work in progress, a book called* The Known *about a Canadian woman's experience with witchcraft in Mexico.*

The Produce Palace

STEVE KELLER

On Fridays, I celebrate the differences between the North American culture in which I was raised and the Mexican culture in which I now live. I do that by shopping for groceries.

A twenty-minute drive from my house in the country brings me to the center of San Miguel de Allende, where my shopping begins, usually at a store I call "The Produce Palace."

The store doesn't really have a name; it doesn't even have a sign. The only clues from the street as to its nature are the stacks of plastic bins of *jicamas*, grapefruits, and sweet potatoes that flank the entry steps. I call it the "Produce Palace" so my wife and I have a name for the place, and to satisfy my sense of irony: produce the place certainly offers, in abundance, but it's hardly a palace.

The store occupies a space that is far too tiny for its merchandise and its employees and its customers. Within that space, and overflowing from it, is a comprehensive assortment of fresh fruits and vegetables; dried beans, eggs, dried chiles. A few canned goods are also available.

As I enter, climbing a couple of steps between the sentry-like stacked bins, I am confronted with tiers of tilted bins stacked to nearly six feet, generally vegetables on the wall to my left and fruits on the back wall. Shelves almost too high to reach run along the walls above the bins: those on my left contain celery, spinach, chard, and leeks. Those straight ahead contain pineapples and papayas. A free-standing, glass-fronted refrigerated case about six feet wide extends from the wall on the right. The only clear horizontal space in the entire store is between the two digital scales that sit atop the case. Bins for which there are no other spaces sit on the floor, shoved against others in the tiers or against the refrigerated case.

One reason I shop there is that it is practically next door to Super Bonanza, a store worthy of an essay in its own right. Here I need only say that Bonanza, though a small store, offers the widest variety of groceries in San Miguel, vastly greater than that of any of the town's three supermarkets. Because of its extensive array of spices, dried fruits, nuts, specialty vinegars, imported cheeses, capers, and prepared curries, my shopping excursions almost always include a trip to Bonanza as well.

I shop at the Produce Palace because I like the people who run the place. I shop there because the store usually provides me with high quality produce. Not always, to be sure, and not everything I require. Sometimes, for example, there's not a red bell pepper in the place that's free of the wrinkles of old age.

But I've learned to ask when I don't find what I need; more often than not, it's available, but stored away. Unlike Safeway in the States, where employees strive continuously to present only the most beautiful produce, here in Mexico the aging merchandise is kept on display in the hope that it will sell before it has to be discarded. There may be a box of beautiful fresh red peppers waiting to replace whichever of those wrinkled ones on display finally die of old age, but it is necessary to ask.

I have developed other strategies for shopping at the Produce Palace. First, I have honed my sadistic urges so finely that I now derive pleasure from elbowing aside little old ladies. Second, I have learned to stake out a territory, perhaps among the guavas or other slow-moving merchandise, where I can stash my carefully selected treasures as they accumulate. And finally, I have become adept at thrusting my selections into the space on top of the refrigerated case, the space that serves as the check-out area, as soon as I've finished shopping. I sometimes use elbows in implementing this strategy as well.

I was lucky yesterday because I shopped when there were almost no other customers. With the proprietor and two or more employees weighing and tallying purchases, lugging in fresh merchandise, and rearranging what's already there, the place is crowded before the first customer arrives. When there are several other shoppers, the usual situation, I often have to wait just to get a plastic bag, then wait again until the person in front of me has finished pawing through the tomatoes.

I spent 200 pesos there yesterday; for me, a new record. This is what my 200 pesos bought:

1/2 bunch of celery

2 large red bell peppers

1 green bell pepper

About two pounds of carrots

A pound or so of limes

A cucumber

3 large white onions

18 plum tomatoes

2 large bunches of spinach

3/4 pound of mushrooms

2 large avocados

1 huge bunch of radishes

A dozen small grapefruits

Almost a pound of broccoli

2 huge leeks

1 small head of Romaine lettuce

3 small bananas

2 small mangoes

I may be forgetting something, but I think the point is clear: that's a lot of food for the equivalent of about fifteen dollars U.S. What's more, the proprietor threw in a large orange papaya to sweeten the deal.

Gringos in San Miguel, conditioned by experiences of "one-stop shopping" that supermarkets in the United States so successfully provide, often shop in similar stores in Mexico. But it isn't the same here: a supermarket of 15,000 square feet that offers automotive tires and batteries, home furnishings, appliances large and small, clothing, paints and hardware, and has a snack bar and a coffee shop, in addition to the usual assortment of groceries, might be out of carrots. And the "fresh" food offered there might be well past its prime. I generally avoid Mexican supermarkets.

Besides, the proprietors of the Produce Palace are a family; their faces are as familiar to me as mine is to them. I suspect they're making a good living out of their store. I hope so. I'm doing my part. I'd much rather do business with that family than give custom to Super Megapesos.

The Produce Palace truly fills my needs. I find good merchandise there, at excellent prices. It's convenient. I do business with people who have faces. And it's so totally, thoroughly Mexican.

My life would be poorer without that store.

Postscript: Since I wrote the foregoing, in July 2009, the Produce Palace has not only moved to a much more spacious location, but has also acquired a name, one I would never have guessed. I mention these facts only in passing, because they do not enhance this tale in any way other than to remove the experiences recounted above from the present and to relegate them to the past, the past of nostalgia, the past from which they may be recalled, perhaps improved, with every retelling.

The store is certainly easier to deal with, and there may well be fewer little old ladies around town with bruised ribs, but I can't help thinking that something has been lost.

Steve Keller's upbringing commenced in the U.S., mostly in Colorado, and continues in San Miguel. He believes we Gringos have a lot to learn from Mexicans.

Today Guanajuato Is Better

JANNA STEIN

J t's unexpected. One minute you're sitting alone on Omar's roof watching the sun go down behind the jagged skyline and worrying that the dog is actually poisoning herself with that plastic cup she's eating. The next minute, all you want is to buy a solitary *caguama* from Marta's store and hear Jose Alfredo Jimenez' voice pouring out from your small speakers into the approaching night.

The dog is chasing her tail. I am crying, but this is OK. Like a tattoo, this is indulgent pain. I have all the leisure and freedom in the world to turn this rooftop into a lonesome cantina, to love the two warm tears that I feel on my cheeks. I, by chance, was not born a *güera*, a *gringa*, a *gabacha* so I don't have to work taking down the *lonas* at the closing marketplace or push my wobbly cart home up the hill on Cuesta de San Jose. I am never so tired that all I want is to fall down on a lumpy bed and sleep until I have to wake up and do it all over again. I am lucky. There is nothing luckier than to be sitting here above the street lamps, among the leaves of the park trees, and crying.

Damn small towns and all their emotional surprises. I wonder if he saw me. Probably not. Look up anywhere in San Miguel and you see a hundred rooftops. But there I was, with my fingers gripping the chain-link fence (it protects us from falling off) like a kid in a Chicago backyard, curious about what all the music was. Down on the street, he was dancing with some breathless, windswept girl. They jostle their way through the crowd, laughing. He spins her and she almost falls. She throws her arms around his neck to catch herself. They're having fun.

He couldn't always dance, I remember. Once he took me to the ocean and, at a beach like a flower blossom, he said, "*Enseñarme cómo se baila la cumbia.*"

I laughed at him. That was three years ago. He must have picked something up since then. I don't keep track of all his comings and goings.

The dog bites my sandal and I yell at her because once he taught me how to drive *estandar* and then he let me sit out the window while he drove the car out to the empty, sun-browned field to practice. That same day, we sat on the sidewalk in a town where herds of sheep still march down the street with as much purpose and entitlement as pedestrians. We drank dusty beers together as naturally as if we had been there forever.

That's why I yelled at the dog.

In the sheep-town, there had been a gigantic mural painted on one of the downtown's chipping walls. The ironic words painted on it were these: *¡HOY GUANAJUATO ES MEJOR!*

That was the gorgeous view we enjoyed as we sat on the sidewalk and joked about ourselves, 50 years from now. When he left, I told him, "*Hoy Guanajuato es mejor porque tu no vas a estar.*"

A long time's gone by since then. I'd heard he'd returned, taken a gray and yellow bus from the coast until the palm trees *se volvieron nopales.*

Now I watch him disappear into the parade of locos. I think of Marta and her kind, round face and her cold glass bottles of beer. As I search for the dog's leash, the people on the street are getting further away. They are a mass of color in the narrow streets, lapping at the walls of the houses like the ocean on red rocks.

Without the town of San Miguel, it is safe to say that Janna Stein would never have come into being. Her parents, both American authors, met there in the 1970s. Her family has been traveling back and forth from Chicago to San Miguel for as long as she can remember. Janna's oldest friendships are rooted in San Miguel. She clambered around the fountain in Bellas Artes as a child with the same people she drinks with at the Cuca today. San Miguel is home to her family, her heart and her inspiration.

Soledad

ALISON BASTIEN

I t's a regular weekday in San Miguel: stuck almost at a standstill in mid-afternoon traffic on Zacateros, one of the main streets that leads out of town. Cars are stalled as far ahead of us as we can make out.

"It's a funeral car heading for the *panteon,*" my husband informs, craning his neck out the window. "There ought to be a law..."

I laugh, then I wonder what could he mean? A law against dying? A law against funerals? The irony is that he, the Mexican half of us, is annoyed.

"Too busy to stop for death?" I tease.

"Just look at this!" he fumes, as the cars behind us begin to honk. " See? It's a mess."

We *should* stop for death, or at least slow down. It's just hard to tell if it's coming or going around here. Next door to my home, where I work, is a funeral home/carpentry shop. Behind its plate glass windows are displayed all sizes and shapes of coffins; the white shoebox size for the babies, the grey silk with tafetta and tassels, brass handles, the brass hand-carved wood lacquered to a sheen.

Our street is on the way to the cemetery, several blocks further down. Many times I've said excitedly to my children: Look! It's a parade! Look! Look, it's the *danzantes!* It's the *mariachis!* Girls, hurry, it's the circus! Out we'd run to the street only to see that it *was* one of the above, followed by a hearse, with a bunch of droopy people shuffling behind it.

"Oh," the girls would say, disappointed, "no, it's not. It's just a dead guy."

We had a housekeeper when our kids were young. My husband and I were in our early thirties and Doña Soledad was in her early forties, which made her the proxy mother figure to us all. She walked over in the mornings from the Colonia San Antonio, a few blocks away, looking at once middle-aged and frumpy in her tee shirt and sweat pants and utterly cool in her aviator sunglasses and ambling stride. Every other week, her short hair would be in a new style. I never knew there were so many things that could happen to short hair: suddenly with blonde streaks, suddenly not, suddenly curly, suddenly layered. Her neighbor was in beauty school and she was the guinea pig.

One day, she mentioned a pain in her abdomen, indicating a spot sort of off to the right below her belly button. I had been a midwife for many years and I knew a bit about anatomy.

"Oh yeah?" I asked. "Like what?"

"It's like a blop. It gets all inflamed. It's worse mostly on the new moon," she said, rubbing a spot under her t-shirt. It really hurts sometimes. I've been to the doctor and taken this and that."

"What'd the doctor say?"

"It's probably this or that," she'd say.

We had this conversation, or variations on the theme, every few weeks.

Then I'd suggest a new approach: how about this or that remedy, this food, this compress, this whatever. She'd say, I'm going to go see this guy or that.

Nothing was helping. She'd even gone to El Seguro, the bigger Social Security hospital in Celeya, missing a day of work and returning to report having taken the bus, then waiting five hours, then, when it was her turn, they'd say the doctor wasn't there now, to come back next week. This happened twice, even with an appointment. I'd say: I'll pay for you to see a different doctor, the specialist, or the homeopath....

Here, there. Months, maybe a year, went by of this. The pain would get slightly better. It would would come back. Opinions would be cast. Diagnosis declared. Treatments proffered.

One day, standing by the wall calendar in our tiny kitchen, Doña Soledad said, *Señora*, I've decided the only thing left to do is get the operation. The last three doctors agree it's some kind of a hernia. Maybe from my Cesarean sections. There's this Doc I'm seeing at the Seguro Social — I trust him. He said he'll operate on me and give me a discount. I'm going to do it. On this day." She pointed to the square number 23 in the month of May.

"You sure?" I asked. She was. So she did.

It was very hot that May. I went with my youngest to visit her in the clinic after her operation. We entered through a garage, then into a dark little space where three women lay in three narrow beds, sweating. One was Doña Sole.

"You did it!" I smiled, clutching her hand and trying not to squeeze the I.V. Tube. "It's done! Your suffering is over now! You're on the other side!"

I hate now that I said that. She died that night, quite suddenly. They had sent her home and, at three in the morning, one of her daughters called us, very distraught.

"Help! Help! Mom's having trouble breathing! We've called an ambulance!"

We arrived at the clinic just as a figure was literally running out of the garage and into the street.

"Hey, isn't that her doctor?" I asked my husband.

"Hey! Doctor! What's happening to our friend? Where are you going? Hey! *You!*" shouted my husband as we watched the doctor, white coat and all, race to his car, glance back at us as he fumbled the key in the ignition and drove off.

"Uh oh," said my husband.

We entered the garage into the waiting area. There, a small cluster of Soledad's relatives informed us she was dead on arrival.

"*Y el doctor?*" Everyone shrugged.

"*Y* Doña Soledad?" I asked. They motioned to another door. I indicated I'd like to go in and received a nod of assent before I even knew what I was doing.

Soledad means solitude, or lonlieness, in Spanish.

Alone she was, on a gurney, covered head to toe by a thin sheet. Being a midwife, I was accustomed to life and death, to people coming or going out of thier bodies. I wasn't afraid. I could feel her essence was still thickly hanging around her, for about three or four feet out around her body. I tentatively pulled back the sheet, in order to see her face, and then suddenly decided not. I wanted to remember her face in life, not in death. I held onto a lock of her hair. I cried a while. I stroked her hair, assured her we would look out for her children and how much we all loved her.

Eventually, some guy opened the door and stood there looking at me in a state I couldn't interpret — maybe he was in deep grief. Maybe he couldn't believe this *gringa* was in there talking on and on to a dead person, or more specifically, to the person's hair.

It was so very hot that May. I didn't go to the *velorio* that was held in their house. My husband did. He told me she was in the open casket set up in their driveway. People came day and night, and sat on folding chairs. They prayed, and ate and drank and told stories. They cried, they laughed. They chatted.

"It's too hot for this kind of thing," my husband reported. "The sons had to keep bringing bags of ice to pack around the coffin to keep her fresh."

The actual funeral was preceded by a *misa* in the church. They said a lot about God and not much about Soledad. But she was there, in the front. The casket was closed now. When the service was over, I shuffled out, crying like everyone else.

As I was leaving, a bride and groom were arriving. The bride was young and gorgeous in white, clickety-clacking in her heels as she passed the coffin, which was being shouldered by eight sweating men.

How bittersweet, I thought, as I noted a group of *mariachis*, all in white, arriving after the bridal pair. Life, too, won't stop long for Death. But, to my suprise, the *mariachis* did not follow Life. They lifted thier horns and strummed their guitars to lead the way for Death. They took their places at the head of Doña Soledad's procession to the graveyard, playing beautiful love ballads all the way.

At the cemetery, they formed a semi-circle around the grave and the relatives formed another circle. There was a pile of dirt and a grave marker already stuck by the rectangular hole. In fact, I realized, there was already a coffin in the hole. And Doña Soledad was being stacked right in there on top of it. Another marker, wrought iron with a big heart, was then affixed right above the other cross.

I didn't understand. At all.

I let the house go to pot. I was so sad, so confused. Why did that doctor run away as if it were a crime scene and not his own clinic? Why did Doña Soledad die suddenly when she'd been well enough to go home only hours before? Was it an embolism? A heart attack? Did some stitches come undone and cause an internal bleed? She'd gone to a hundred doctors over several years with this. Why did she pick this one? I kept seeing it over and over in my mind's eye, her pointing to the date on the calendar in my kitchen, choosing, unknowingly, the date she would die.

I had three kids and my work in my house, and it was a mess.

One day, not long after Soledad died, I stumbled and spilled a bunch of salt on my living room rug. I crumpled to my knees and swatted lamely at the salt, pushing it into a pile on the rug. There is a saying in Mexico: *Hechar la sal* which literally means, to throw salt on something or someone, which metaphorically means to mess it up, or do them harm. Things felt very messed up. The spill reminded me I had no maid to help me clean the house. Which reminded me for the millionth time that Soledad was dead.

This is how her daughters found me, this strange person, on her knees, sobbing over a pile of salt. They were banging on my front door, which, like the entire wall, is made of plate glass so I could see their faces: open-mouthed and looking a little afraid.

They introduced themselves as Doña Soledad's daughters. Their father had said that I had told him that I could give them work. I had never met them before. I didn't realize they were so old. One was 18 and looked a lot like Soledad. The other was 20, and didn't look much like her at all.

In the conversation that followed, it was explained to me that the eldest was actually the daughter of Soledad's *comadre,* her dear freind, who had died in childbirth. Soledad had taken the newborn and nursed and raised it along with her own children.

"She's the one mom's buried with," the elder girl said shyly. "My real mom. The cemetery was full so we buried my moms together."

"Oh," I said, barely comprehending. And then I realized though, in this case, it was good. Soledad would never really be alone.

Postscript: Her daughters worked for us for many years — even as they married and had children of their own. One still works with us, in fact, fifteen years later. She brings her youngest, who is one year old, to work with her. None of us really understand what happened to Soledad. But, in any event, none of us suffers her loss in solitude. Those who left and those who stayed, continue to overlap one another's lives.

Alison Bastien has worked with plants , women and birth for over thirty years in San Miguel. Her writings on these subjects have been published in Midwifery Today *magazine since 1984, and some of her essays appear in other anthologies on childbirth. You can see some of her work at* lavictoriana.com, *including the shop she and her husband, Helio, have run for over 19 years.*

Maine To Mexico

JAN BAUMGARTNER

Getting here from there is nothing short of a milagro. Getting anywhere from Maine is a test in patience, resilience, and a strip search of your sanity. One might call it Sanity Profiling; if you have any trace of it left as you flee the remoteness and bitter cold, you will not escape before questioning if you are fit to be let loose in the outside world. Dribbling, a lobster bib may be in order.

Coming from the winter drab of a frigid and nearly colorless Maine, the Mexican tsunami of bright and dizzying colors, the daily Christmas *posadas* and parades, nearly necessitate a Dramamine. My equilibrium needs adjusting. Mexicans celebrate just about everything. And with a little good-natured arm twisting, even the most absurd event might warrant a firecracker, colored streamers, or a tequila shooter with a Squirt chaser. They are unapologetic in their belief that celebration and gratitude can be found in what others might find mundane, insignificant. They find the extraordinary in the every day. Between the singing and fireworks, the explosion of celebratory "bombs" at dawn, the radios and rumbas and lilting *mariachis*, barking dogs and church bells, you can't help but feel more alive than you might like, especially at five in the morning. It is exhausting. And, it is life affirming.

A Funeral Procession

On my second day in my small apartment in San Miguel de Allende, I heard singing. From my rooftop terrace that affords sweeping views of the seventeenth-century Parroquia church, Las Monjas, Bellas Artes, city lights, countryside and mountain peaks, I watched as a small procession of mourners trailed behind a hearse draped with white lilies. Thirty or so people walked up the ancient cobbled street, softly singing. It was not a sorrowful melody. There was no weeping. It was a sound of acceptance. Young and old dressed in casual clothes, parents holding toddlers and infants sang a tune as familiar and comforting as time immemorial. It was the celebration of life; the acceptance of death. There was no fanfare; just the simple reminder that even in death, life goes on.

Their singing co-mingled with music drifting from the *jardín*. The music was lively and, as on many days, people may have been dancing. Just a block away there was a car turning the corner with its radio blasting. The sky was bright, the air warm, the sun full. The energy ran from musician to dancer to driver, to mourner and passerby, and those bearing witness. I do not know who passed on, but being present at that moment, I, as all the others, became part of the celebration.

A Pick-Up

I am laden with the days' bounty. My straw basket is filled with part of tonight's meal; avocados, tortillas, a wedge of Manchego, olives and wine. It is hot and I am still adjusting to the mile high altitude, the relentless sun, and the antiquated cobbled streets that are treacherous at the best of times even in the most unattractive of sensible shoes.

He is standing on the corner of Correo and Sollano. My pace is brisk. I am sweaty and hungry and a bit breathless. Perhaps he mistakes my panting and dripping "glow" as overly friendly pheromones. He steps in front and offers a forceful "*¡Hola, buenas tardes!*" "Do I know you?"

It is not deliberate, but I am sure my eyes roll behind my sunglasses. "No," I say weaving my way around him. He continues, "Do you live here?" He pushes, "I'm thinking of moving here from Mexico City. Do you like it here? My name is Rodrigo. I'm a pianist. I'm performing at one of the local theaters, perhaps you'd like to come. Are you an artist? You look like an artist. I like your vest. What did you say your name is?" Way too much information, I think. "I didn't," I reply. He asks me my name. "Juana," as I pick up my pace. "Oh, Juanita," he prefers. I am not feeling *ita-light* in any way. In fact, I am feeling more *Juan-ish* as I feel *cojones* developing as I ready myself to politely say "shove off."

He is walking backwards now, unfettered. I am making him work for it or maybe this is how he gets his exercise each day. I'm in no mood, in fact when hungry, I can get testy. "Don't worry," he insists, "I am not following you," as he follows me the length of Sollano. "I was going this way anyway."

I must admit, I am impressed with his agility, his near tightrope finesse in negotiating these malevolent cobbles, and backwards no less while carrying on feeble pick-up lines that are equally as unremarkable when delivered in a foreign accent. He is not concerned about traffic behind him, dangerous gutters, horse, dog and burro droppings that are large enough to act as violent speed bumps. If nothing else, he is a brave man. Finally, he realizes I am not interested when I bid him an avocado firm "*Adios,*" and he heads back from where he started.

Maybe someday the man who walks backwards up cobbled streets will run into a woman walking backwards down cobbled streets and they will catch each other from falling into the antiquated gutter. It will be love at first sight, only backwards. Life is sweeter when surprised.

A Pink *Pinata*

It is 9:30 at night and from the terrace, the lights of the church spirals are magnificent. The air is soft and warm. I have been admiring, too, the thin bands of Christmas lights that adorn the facades along my street — they are not garish but simple red, green and white strands. Children are laughing. I hear singing. I lean over my terrace wall and look up the length of Terraplen to see a children's birthday party at the end of the block. A few dozen children are clustered in tight knots in the center of the street, the intersection blocked off by small bodies. Strung up from one side of the street to the other is a rope that drapes from one window to the next. Hanging from the middle of the rope is a pink burro *piñata*. The children are singing louder now and wielding a broom. They are taking turns at pummeling the *piñata*.

Cars drive up the street and then slowly back down, turn corners, finding different routes toward their destinations. There are no honking horns, shouting voices, only the unspoken understanding that a child's birthday party and a pink burro *piñata* take precedence over traffic and for tonight, hold court at this intersection.

The children sing and howl with laughter. The broom is slicing wild shards through still air as they miss the prancing *piñata*. Finally, after numerous attempts, the burro is broken; its pink head still strung on the clothes line, the paper body breaking away and open spilling candy and small toys into the center of the street. The children scream and scramble. Pockets and mouths are filled with sweets.

A gray street dog stands against a brown and yellow house. He too was watching the children swat at the *piñata*. The dog is smiling. He is happy he is not a pink burro.

Pastel de Chocolate

I have a friend who lives just one block up. He is my *pastel de chocolate* friend. He tells me I use "too many words and think too much," and implies that I have surpassed my word count. He insists that I over-analyze everything, beleaguer the process and, as he recently said, "just think if you got frequent flyer miles for the long journeys you take." He may be right. So instead of talking, we eat cake.

My first day here, my landlord shared a secret; the best chocolate cake in town is sold twice a week at the *tienda* just two doors up from my apartment. I don't believe her. The *tienda* is small and stocked with basics; water, eggs, sodas, bar soap, a few avocados, sugar, toilet paper. But chocolate cake? "Yeah, right," my friend says, "the best cake in town? Who makes it, Sara Lee?"

It arrives at the *tienda* during evening hours, under the cover of darkened skies. Sometimes it is tardy and those of us with sweet teeth can be found pacing nearby like junkies in need of a fix. My friend picks up the stash. He is my connection, our dirty little secret, and he scores the goods and delivers directly to my front door. In the shadow of night, he arrives with a small paper plate swelling with the inflated creamy richness of mile high chocolate cake. It is not brown. It is black. It is as black as a cat.

He stands beneath the golden light of the street lantern holding the *pastel*, a fragile white plastic fork standing upright in the middle of the frosting battleground, a premature surrender. "Hellohh, luvah," I purr to the object of my affection, not the man bearing my desire. The second night of the score, he looks both worried and relieved. "It was the last piece," he whispers, holding the melt-in-your-mouth slab before me. He looks as though he's just secured the last dose of Tamiflu during an H_1N_1 outbreak. We are grateful for small things; at least those draped in icing.

There is no need to talk. But somehow I manage, "You know this might be even better with just a pinch of *chipotle* powder," but I realize I'm toying with perfection, not to mention his nerves. He ignores me as he fills his mouth with frosting and closes his eyes. This moist, black *pastel* needs no words. Other than an occasional moan, whimper or sigh, no noun, verb, dangling participle or chad can do it justice. Some things in life cannot be defined, only experienced.

Our friendship is made of something that can be poured into a sheet pan. Our foundation is batter. Truth be told, if this *pastel de chocolate* ever ceased to be delivered, I'm not sure what we'd miss more, each other or the chocolate cake. I don't ponder too long on the thought, however, as I have enough mind-trip frequent flyer miles to circumnavigate the globe many times over and return just in time for the weekly delivery of the sinful pastel. Besides, it is Friday — and there is chocolate in the air.

A Barking Man and a Parrot who Thinks it's a Rooster

Dog barking in San Miguel is as incessant as the church bells. The town is known for its abundance of *perros*, both rib-bare street waifs and those lovingly pampered and dressed in the latest fashions. It is a barking free-for-all most hours of the day and night. So I was surprised when I saw a man walking up my street barking. He only barked twice. Did he think the day had scored low on number of barks? Or was it the tequila barking? He was good. If I hadn't seen him I would have believed he was a dog.

On the opposite side of the street, tucked two buildings in from a bright lemon yellow *casa* and a sunset coral *casa*, is a large pomegranate-colored *casa*. Actually, it looks more like a big bowl of *salsa*. Its grand arched terrace faces my diminutive bird's nest. The terrace is always in the shadows. I hear things from those shadows. A friend told me that the elderly woman "keeps" animals, exotic birds, parrots, macaws, even monkeys. I think I hear the parrot.

In the distance near San Juan de Dios church, a rooster caws each morning and early evening. It is a soft, non-abrasive cawing that lilts on the shifting breeze and mixes with cooking smells and flowers. The parrot mimics the rooster. He, like the barking man, is very convincing. The parrot sounds more like a rooster than the rooster. The Barking Man and the Rooster Parrot could have a show in the *jardín*. But the real star would be...

Drama Cat

I heard her first. I say "her" because no male cat could swing such a drama queen performance and get away with it. And she's Siamese. Female Siamese are known for their over-the-top performances and piss-poor attitudes. I've known a few.

Her guttural howling went from sheer annoyance at the imperfection and mediocrity of the world below, to the pleading, gasping rants and moans of a cat ready to jump. It startled me. She seemed to be bemoaning, "*¡Donde esta de agua! mi leche! mi pollo! mi pastel de chocolate!*"

The white and shadow-tinged minx paced back and forth on the narrow ledge of the *casa* across the street, at times, placing her tiny, fragile, razor-sharp claws so close to edge I wanted to yell, "Stop! Don't jump!" but in her disdain and contempt, she'd move back an inch, tease then howl, teeter at the brink again, only to retreat, swinging her bony bottom back into the cover of potted plants where she was probably drooling on a rubber toy or swatting at ants. Did I really think that a cat jumping from a roof terrace to some ten feet below would be catastrophic? Or was her performance just that convincing? She shall now be referred to as Meryl. Or Merylita.

A few days into her theatrics, I caught her napping. One late afternoon from my sun-drenched terrace, I caught her in full repose, and for what and who she really is. Her terrace (I say hers because I'm pretty sure she owns the place and rents out rooms) was thick with drying clothes, a white load, socks, panties, and t-shirts all dangling in the breeze like miniature underwear *piñatas*. On the terrace table was a large Coca Cola crate on wheels. It was upside down. She was splayed, unaware, on top of the crate—day dreaming, maybe flat-out snoring. To her right were two empty soda bottles. They looked like Fanta. I'm not suggesting she had drunk the sodas, she is more a tequila cat, only that they added to her stripped down Academy Award performance. She was sleeping, fat and happy. This was as close to a nude scene as she was going to get.

Next time I see her teetering on the edge, howling and threatening to jump, demanding chicken and chocolate cake, I will look her squarely in the eyes and say, "Merylita, I saw you on your back, spread-eagled and snoring. Honey, gig's up. I know you're not jumpin' but I won't tell." It's good to have friends in the neighborhood.

Origins of Laughter

Mexicans and *gringos* laugh differently. From my terrace, if I hear laughter echoing on the cobbled street below, I can see the color of the laughter. *Gringo*s sound lighter. Their color of laughter is of a higher pitch — it flies — it has wings: it is borne of the sky. It is Crimson Yellow. It sounds more carefree. It has the sound and innocence of a child. It is the sound and color of a goldfinch.

Mexicans laugh with a deeper resonance. It is hearty and real and closer to the bone, of the soil. It is richer and feels as if it is harvested from the earth, has roots. I hear it reverberating from the land, deep and earthy and from the heart. It sounds heavier and seems to carry with it a history, an ancient wisdom. To me, Mexican laughter sounds like a spirit bird ~ a raven or crow. It is the color of coffee.

Beginnings and Endings

I have made new friends here. Some are here to stay, others are fleeting, what they are or need to be for the moment, sweet but temporary, like the instant gratification of chocolate cake. You could argue that friendships formed from batter have no real footing, no foundation. But I will not shortchange nor dismiss the power of chocolate. The cocoa bean was once more valuable than gold.

Others, like small *milagros*, happen upon you when you least expect them, good luck charms found in once empty pockets, and surprise you with their depth of meaning and forever after.

Friendships should have a beginning. Some, though, begin at the end; an ending in progress. If you meet someone and it begins at the end, backwards, can you start over, at the beginning, knowing how the story ends? Or do second chances not exist if there never was a start?

Marking Time by Church Bells

There is no clock in my apartment. In fact, it is short on many things, but I make do just fine. My first day, I complained to a friend that there was no cutting knife, only butter knives, and only three forks. "How many forks do you need?" he asked.

I have an old watch that I wear only when traveling. It sits upstairs wheezing away the seconds of its ten dollar price tag. But I always know the time, or close to it, by the church bells, and without the added weight of the world strapped around my wrist.

The church bells ring on the hour and the half. So I am always within 30 minutes of the correct time. Whatever that is. Not knowing the exact time is like laughter ~ it too has wings ~ it's sweeter than cake.

A native Californian, Jan Baumgartner is a writer/editor living along the coast of Downeast Maine. Her background includes travel writing for The New York Times *and comedy writing for the N. California Emmy Awards. She has worked as a grant writer in the fields of academia, AIDS, and wildlife conservation for NGO's in the U.S. and Africa. Her articles and essays have appeared in numerous online and print publications including the* NYT, Bangor Daily News, Open Salon, OpEdNews.com, Banderas News Puerto Vallarta, *and* Scoop New Zealand. *Her essays on Mexico are included in two anthologies. In addition to working on a memoir about her husband's death from ALS, her solo travels and life in Africa and Mexico, she is editing a memoir written by the founder and president of the Awareness Foundation for OCD.*

The Painter of San Miguel

MARIANNE WERNER

I walk cobblestone streets,
ring Calle Jesús 42,
and enter another world.
This small home and studio
belong to an Indian painter,
un amor de mi madre,
one love of my mother
for many years.

He has dozens and dozens
of paintings—covering the walls,
leaning against his bed,
lining the narrow stairs:
many are like carnival—
toy people, whimsical,
medieval figures with doll-like
box faces and short bodies;
some are filled with stories, dreams,
a magic of dark and pale colors.

This place is an artifact—
hanging crystals, red Christmas balls,
broken pieces of pottery, masks,
old, old pictures, and displays

of patterned found art.
We walk upstairs
to find more paintings,
and on the wall I see
a collage with pictures
of my mother:
as a child, in high school,
as a younger woman
sitting under a tree—
always at ease, with a smile.

The painter talks about the past,
how he misses my mother
and how when he, too, is gone,
perhaps someone will make
a museum of his home.
He asks, Who will remember
his days in Michoacán
with my mother? Who will
understand the ghosts in his dreams
that make him begin canvas
after canvas? Who will speak
of his mother's bones protected
by the nuns until he could bury them?
Who, he asks, who will tell *his* story?

Marianne Werner came to San Miguel by way of her mother, Lois, who first discovered its magic in the late 70s and continued to live here on and off until her death in 2001. Marianne visits San Miguel when she can, trying to understand her mother in the process. She retired recently after teaching high school English for 25 years, and then at Butte College in Chico, CA for 13 years. She has been writing poetry since high school and has had poems published in various literary magazines. Marianne has written travel articles for her local paper and recently has branched out to creative non-fiction and photography. Her passion is travel, especially in Africa. She hopes to be able to continue traveling until her last breath...lingering periodically in San Miguel for renewal!

First Steps

JUDYTH HILL

In centro, children skitter in curbside push-pull.
Evening translates into Cathedral.
I become lucid in bells, bilingual in apse and nave.
I look always for love, buy tin horse-drawn toys,
all gleam and spin.

I have come somewhere rich in *carnitas* and happenstance,
a wealth of tortillas, maize, and *escobas*, sweeping, sweeping.
Leaves scatter and fall on cobblestone, their dip and roll,
round rock roads, and steep.
I walk and lose myself ever easily in luxurious tilt.

It is effortless, this vanish.
I cross cultures and corners, and never see anything twice.
Have two languages to forget in.
All my verbs in the present tense.

You have lost me, or I, you.
It hardly matters, I earn my confusion honestly.
Last light on the coral spires of the Parroquia,
Looking, as ever, like an elaborate wedding cake for God.

I want to marry God, that's why I have come, some hope
of co-habitation

in the household of Holy.
It's here, and I am too.

Between the sound of horns, *besos*, and blessings,
mucho gustos and bay laurel press shoulder to shoulder in the *jardín*.
Mariachis play, and this is real, I promise.

I live in Mexico, and have no idea how I came to do such a thing.

My own life shocks me.
I dress always oddly and can't find streets I've walked for years
in dreams,
Everywhere so nearly familiar!

I do have a grammar of clocktime, could parse the yesterday that
led me here:
to a bench facing southwest and beatific, baskets of zinnias
and *girasoles*,
to *elotes*, dripping *mantequilla* and red chile, Michoacán ices in
white paper cups
with soft folds,
sweet *refrescos*, and you.

There's legitimacy in my wandering.
When have I ever known where I am, anyway?
Finally, I surrender.
Become buoyant with happiness, remember the secret of being lost:
Stay still, wait
To be found.

Cielito Lindo, the music reminds,
and the sun strikes a luminous bargain of warmth on rose walls.
Maps are not needed.
I know where an archangel lives, and the future.
That is enough direction for one night.

Judyth Hill is a performance poet and teacher of poetry, living in a flower-filled valley outside San Miguel de Allende at Simple Choice Farm, her working farm and Artist Retreat. Judyth is Poet-in-Residence for museums and schools across the USA. She teaches writing online, at conferences, offers a weekly poetry class in San Miguel, and is the recipient of numerous Foundation awards and fellowships. Her six published books of poetry include Men Need Space, Presence of Angels *and* Black Hollyhock, First Light. *She is the author of the internationally acclaimed poem,* Wage Peace. *She is the author of the cookbook,* Geronimo, *from Ten Speed Press, and an internationally published journalist. Her newest book,* The Sensual Chocolatier, *is forthcoming from Gibbs Smith Publishing, in Spring, 2011. She was described by the St. Helena Examiner as, "Energy with skin," and* The Denver Post *as, "A tigress with a pen."*

Frances Goes Home

MARCIA LOY

or the last time, Frances Lang looked at the scenery from the window of the bus, enjoying the colonial architecture and the vivid colors of the buildings, with bougainvillea spilling over the walls in shades of ochre, sienna, orange, rose and apricot. Jacaranda trees spread their purple flowers over the landscape in mid-spring, which for San Miguel de Allende, Mexico, was the middle of March.

Frances was the only *gringa* on the number 13 bus, headed for the *tianguis*, the traveling market. The bus stopped past the *glorieta* — the traffic circle — and many passengers got off, including Frances. At 5'7", she was taller than most of the Mexican women around her. She crossed the pedestrian bridge over the busy traffic below, her gray hair shimmering in the sunlight, carrying a large mesh bag in red and green plaid, ubiquitous in San Miguel. Her heart started to pound as she approached the *tianguis*. In the three years she'd lived in San Miguel, the traveling market, set above the town on large paved squares, had become her favorite weekly event. At daybreak each Tuesday morning, vendors set up tables, offering everything Frances could imagine: school supplies, household goods, DVDs and music CDs, electronics, shoes, plants and flowers, tools, beans, produce, hair ribbons, furniture, jewelry and canned goods. A corner table offered fresh French bread, pastries and sweet rolls. Vendors cooked fresh fish, potato chips, *gorditas* — hot flat bread filled with meats, cheese and vegetables. Others sold *chicharrones* — fried pork rind—and one long stall had fresh juice: pineapple, orange, carrot, rice milk and grapefruit in a Styrofoam cup or a plastic bag tied with a straw sticking out. In a street between the squares, a man with a wheel barrow sold honey; another hawked batteries and shoe laces

Tables piled high with used clothing drew crowds of Mexicans and *gringos* alike. Frances found a rose-colored long cotton dress for 20 pesos — about $1.50 — that looked brand new. At another table she found a pair of jeans, the most difficult item to buy at the market. She had to sort through stacks of jeans to find the right size, color and style, check them for holes or stains and hold them up to her hips to make sure they'd fit.

"Hello, Frances," said Hannah Washburn, a tall woman who favored large jewelry and bright colors. They had met at the monthly luncheons of Mujeres en Cambio, a group that raised money to send girls from the rural areas around San Miguel to school.

"Find some treasures today?" Hannah said.

"A couple. I just saw a rust-colored sweater with silver beads that reminded me of you."

She led Hannah back to the table with the sweater. After paying for it, Hannah said, "Have you been over to the 15-peso tables?"

Frances shook her head. "Let's go."

They browsed the tables for a while, holding up flashy dresses and size-two miniskirts for a laugh. Hannah bought several colorful tops and Frances found a white Chico's shirt.

"How's Peg?" Hannah said.

"I haven't seen her in months," Frances said, looking through a stack of t-shirts.

"What are you talking about? I thought you and Peg were best friends."

"No," Frances said.

"What about cooking for Comida Con Amor?"

"I resigned."

"In that case I hope I can talk you into volunteering for Mujeres en Cambio. We've had some attrition," Hannah said, paying for a long-sleeved pink and aqua blouse dotted with sequins.

"I can't," Frances said, "I'm going back to the States on Saturday."

"How long will you be gone?"

"I'm not coming back."

Hannah stared at her.

"I'm surprised, I thought you loved it here. You told me once you felt San Miguel was heaven."

Frances hesitated. "Living here's not working out like I'd hoped. I miss things from the U.S."

"Like what?"

"I don't know." She shrugged. "Early spring days when the daffodils are in bloom, hot pastrami sandwiches."

Frances reached across the table for a pair of silk slacks and held them to her hips.

"What's going on with you?"

"I've finished my term as chair of the orphanage fund raising," Hannah said.

"Not going to run again?"

"Never," Hannah said. "I want my life back."

"I understand. It's easy to let volunteering take up all your time."

Hannah looked at Frances. "I'll miss you."

"I'll miss you, too, and San Miguel," Frances said, her voice catching.

"Why do I feel like you're not telling me the whole story?"

Frances shrugged.

Hannah gave her a hug and suggested they keep in touch through e-mail. Frances went to her favorite table to buy fruit and vegetables. Juanita always saved her the best red peppers, the largest heads of garlic and the freshest broccoli.

Hannah, she thought, had seen through her. Frances felt embarrassed to tell anyone the real reason she was leaving.

It had to do with Peg and Annabelle. She met Peg shortly after she arrived in San Miguel and they became fast friends, meeting for lunch three times a week, going to garage sales on Saturdays, taking day trips to Guanajuato and Querétaro. They talked on the phone every day.

A new charity had formed to provide lunch for the needy and after talking it over, Peg and Frances signed up to cook three days a week. Neither had experience preparing food for large groups, but they'd had fun transforming recipes for six to lunch for fifty, learning to make huge pots of spaghetti, beans with rice and chicken stew. Frances baked 10 loaves of bread every Monday, Wednesday and Friday. It was demanding, but they loved it. When finished, they went out to lunch as their reward for the hard work.

After a year and a half, Peg introduced Frances to Annabelle. Annabelle and her husband had recently moved to San Miguel from Seattle. Annabelle, a short woman with brown hair who could stand to lose a few pounds, favored baggy cargo pants and polyester shirts, joined them as a cook. The three of them got along like third graders giggling under the oak tree. They all loved to read and recommended books to each other, traded paperbacks and talked about their favorite authors and novels.

Frances couldn't remember the day she realized things weren't the same between them, that there'd been a subtle shift in the dynamic. Peg called on the phone less often, but Frances attributed it to a time crunch, since Peg and her husband were building a house. Frances felt a cool wind at the cooking sessions. The other two didn't talk to her as much as they used to.

One day, Frances ran into a friend and they chatted for a few minutes. At the end of their conversation the woman said, "So long, see you Sunday."

"Sunday?" Frances asked.

"At Peg's housewarming party."

"Oh, sure," Frances said, but Peg hadn't mentioned it to her. Frances' heart sank.

She had bought a gift for the housewarming months earlier. Peg had complained that events in San Miguel often sold t-shirts, but not posters. A San Miguel poster would be fun, Peg said, to hang in the new house. When Frances spotted colorful posters for sale at the jazz fest, she scooped up one and had it matted and framed. She was sorry she hadn't bought one for herself, since it would have looked perfect over her fireplace. The poster had been leaning against a wall in her guest room waiting for the housewarming. Maybe, she decided, Peg just forgot to invite her, but Monday came and went without an invitation. So did Wednesday and Friday. Before that week, she could pretend the coldness was her imagination.

One Wednesday a month later, Peg said she had a dentist's appointment and couldn't do lunch. Annabelle said she'd had a late breakfast and thought she'd go home and transplant geraniums. Frances started to head home but decided to have lunch at La Posadita, one of her favorite restaurants in *centro*. When she walked in, Peg and Annabelle were sitting at a table in the corner. Frances slipped out unseen.

She didn't understand. Had she done something to make them not like her? But what? She began to dread the days they worked together. Headaches and shortness of breath appeared each Monday, Wednesday and Friday morning. As much as she wanted to talk about the problem, she knew Peg hated confrontation and Frances gradually withdrew emotionally.

On her birthday, Peg invited her to lunch. Annabelle was in the States. Peg, a tall, thin woman with fine features, fond of the Atkins diet, ordered a hamburger with cheese and bacon, no bun.

Over coffee, Frances took a deep breath and said, "I value our friendship and I miss it. I don't know what went wrong, but I'd like to fix it if I can."

Peg, rolled a single strand of her long red hair between her thumb and index finger. Her gaze focused on the plants behind Frances. She said, "We have different styles."

"I don't know what that means."

"You go to bed early."

"You don't want to be friends anymore because I go to be early?"

Peg shrugged. "I like to go out at night. I like to eat out. And, afterward, there are plays and concerts and movies. You don't stay up late enough to be of use to me."

Frances sat at the table for a long time after Peg left.

She stuck it out another month, then resigned from the charity. Now, four months later, she'd arranged to move back to the United States. Her landlord had dropped off the new lease, but was on vacation when she made her decision to leave. He was due back on Friday, the day before her departure.

Back at the Tuesday market she bought more fruits and vegetables. It was getting late and she decided to take a cab home. She gave the driver her address on Sollano and sat back as the cab headed down the hills into the city.

She thought about a recent conversation with Frederick Thomas at a party in Guadiana. He was the head of a charity that fed hungry children. She'd heard there was an opening and applied for a job as a cook, but then heard nothing.

"I would have loved to have you cook for my organization," he said.

"I applied for the job," she said. "What happened?"

"When I talked with Annabelle she said you left your last job because you had a busy social life and wanted to enjoy shopping, ladies' lunches and bridge games."

Frances, who hated shopping and never played bridge in her life, realized in that moment that Peg and Annabelle could affect the quality of her life in San Miguel. She decided to return to the States.

Down the hill came the taxi, past the Mirador with its breathtaking view of the city, the dam in the background and mountains in the distance. The driver plunged down one of the narrow, steep streets leading to *el centro*, passing old stone walls with plumbago and trumpet vines cascading down the sides and a little tienda selling soft drinks and snacks. Along the way, she glimpsed a row of her favorite trees, the tall, thin cypresses that always reminded her of Vincent Van Gogh.

A young boy yelled as the cab passed and the driver pulled over. The boy, about nine years old, wearing a clean but old t-shirt and blue jeans meant for someone shorter than he, was crying and pointing to the roof across the street. A small yellow cat meowed plaintively from the roof of a house.

"*Que pasa*, Jávier?" the driver asked.

"*Mi gato*," the boy said.

The driver explained that Jávier was the son of his neighbor and Frances suggested they help.

The man nodded and pulled his cab onto the sidewalk under the roof. He got out and stood on top of the cab but he was too short to get the cat, who continued to meow, while Jávier continued to cry.

"*Necesito un hombre mas alto*," the driver said to her. "We need a taller man."

The driver spoke softly to Jávier until he stopped crying. From a door several houses above them came a young *gringo*, a tall one. Frances explained the problem to him. The *gringo* climbed on the roof of the cab and held out his hands, but he couldn't reach the cat either. He asked Frances to have the driver hand the boy up to him. He held Jávier above his head and the cat jumped in his arms. The four of them hugged each other.

Frances wondered what the chances of this incident happening back in New Jersey. Javier ran home with his small yellow cat and Frances and the cab driver dropped the young American in front of the *jardín*. Frances got out there, too and the driver refused to accept any fare for the ride from the *tianguis*.

Mexican families and retired *gringos* filled the square. Children ran up and down the stairs of the gazebo where bands played on Sunday afternoons. Frances sat down. She watched little boys chase pigeons and thought about the time her car wouldn't start in the parking lot of the Mega supermarket. Two men came over, looked under the hood and tried to help her start it. They worked on her car for half an hour, but neither would take the money she offered them. She thought about the times she'd left her bag, credit card and, once, her camera in restaurants or shops and each time someone came running after her to return the items. She considered the time her friend had gone to Frances' hair stylist and realized, when she went to pay, that her change purse was missing. Marín had not only told her she could pay next time, but offered to lend her money to buy food.

On the way home with her bags, she walked by the Parroquia, the Gothic-style church purportedly designed from a postcard of a European cathedral. Frances opened the gate to her house, stopping to gaze at the fountain built into the front wall of her garden. A canterra lion's head fed water into a large cement half-shell that overflowed into the bottom of the fountain. Her maid had filled the shell with coral roses she'd brought from her own garden. Frances sighed. She went inside, got out her drill and hung the jazz fest poster over her fireplace. It looked gorgeous, as though it had been designed for her living room.

Now, she thought, where did I put the lease?

Marcia Loy was born in Indiana and moved to Miami when she was ten, where she lived for 25 years until she escaped. She and her husband and daughter, Cass, went directly to Chicago because she wanted real weather and Chicago has lots of that. After 30 years in the Windy City, she moved to San Miguel five years ago. She has been active in Mujeres en Cambio, the Literary Sala, the SPA and volunteered at the Biblioteca for several years. She currently facilitates a Writers' Group that meets weekly in San Miguel. Unlike many retirees whose children want them to undergo psychiatric testing when their parents announce their intention to move south of the border, her daughter convinced her to move to Mexico, where she visits often from Minneapolis.

Say, How's the Foot?

Mark Saunders

How San Miguel de Allende Became Known as the City of Fallen Women and Why It Has Nothing To Do with Seduction

San Miguel de Allende is known for many things: as the cradle of Mexican independence, a festival town, an ideal place for artists and art lovers alike, for its year-round spring-like weather. But until you live here you can't fully appreciate why the town is called the "City of Fallen Women," which has nothing to do with seduction and everything to do with the simple yet painful act of falling down and twisting an ankle, not to mention the embarrassment of doing it in public. The streets are steep and narrow, the sidewalks even more so and, for women especially, the mere act of walking can hold unwanted surprises. Of course, there are the usual signs of dogs doing the Scooby doo-doo they do so well, requiring pedestrians to look before every step. And buses or trucks can scrape inches off a walker's belly at no extra charge; the distance between vehicles and humans on a typical side-street in the historic Centroid district is measured in millimeters. Whenever I walk the streets of San Miguel, I'm reminded of the W. C. Fields line where he said it was so crowded at one of his shows people couldn't laugh "ha-ha-ha," they had to laugh "ho-ho-ho."

For the above reasons and more, a cottage shoe industry has sprouted around the treachery of walking in this town. Several shops carry what is known as the "San Miguel Shoe." I am told by women it's that rare fixture in the land of feet: a shoe that is comfortable, stylish and practical. The combination of its rubber soles and thick straps, elastic, of course, ensure that the foot stays securely in place, even while your hat and purse fly off down the street in opposite directions. The shoe is available in bright colors, as well as a classic black, so, as you're falling, those watching will be able to compliment you on how nicely your shoes match the rest of your outfit. Although the San Miguel Shoe may not prevent someone from falling, it could prevent the walker from suffering the further insult of a twisted ankle and, thus, the product has achieved cult status.

Yes, the stones in the street here are cobbled and they can be slippery. So the smart expat uses the raised sidewalks, also made of uneven stone, as the safest place to put down first a left foot, followed by a right one. This pattern of walking works well enough until a store vendor casts soapy water in front of his or her doorway to clean the steps, an event that happens with the frequency of a passing cab. If they were to hold a San Miguel Olympics, one popular event would surely be the Doorway Dash, where competitors would race in front of soapy doorways and the one who didn't fall would win.

The streets and sidewalks in centro can turn a vacation into a hospital visit. Indeed, a common conversation starter is to ask, "How's the foot?" Once you leave the center of town, however, you find streets that are wider and level. Unfortunately, even these streets are unsafe at any speed because of the presence of sudden, inexplicable holes or concrete protrusions in an otherwise smooth surface. So, just when you thought it was safe to walk again, even a level street can trip you up faster than you can say, "San Miguel Shoe." What's a walker to do?

My wife, Arlene, as a case in point, fell three times during our first month here and I suspect her number of missteps is about average.

Arlene's first fall came as the two of us were walking home one afternoon from centro, leaving the picturesque, narrow streets behind us. We had been in centro for la comida, our mid-day meal, and decided to walk home to work off the calories, a leisurely walk that, under normal circumstances, would take about thirty minutes. It was a bright, clear December day. We walked along Ancha de San Antonio, a flat, wide stretch of road that morphs into a highway just south of town. Framed by businesses of all shapes and sizes, from hardware stores to fruit and vegetable stands, roaster chicken shops to espresso hangouts, a Ford dealership and a Cable Television company, the street is like most any street in any mid-sized town in North

America. It's a street made for walking and, if one gets tired, there's always a steady stream of taxis and conveniently-spaced bus stops along the way.

I was walking a few feet ahead of Arlene. I noticed a deep, square-shaped hole in the middle of the sidewalk, bypassed it, and continued on my way. Oblivious as I am, I failed to warn my wife about the hole. Oblivious as she is, she failed to notice it. And to, ahem, twist a popular quote from the Bible: Obliviousness goeth before the fall. I heard a yell and turned to see Arlene bent over as if she were doing a yoga stretch. Fortunately the hole was neatly shaped to fit her shoe size. She simply fell forward like a cut tree and held that pose. I worked to extricate her foot from the hole. At the same time, a local businessman, seeing the accident, rushed out from his office to help. If Arlene had tripped in the United States and a stranger rushed to her aid, there's not doubt in my mind he would have handed her his card and we would have found our first trial lawyer. But this man's concern was genuine and, after he realized Arlene was able to walk, he hailed a cab for us. She had banged her shin and soon it was the size of a softball. Although bruised and in pain, Arlene toughed it out, took two Advils, followed by a shot of gin and by morning the swelling was down. She was back in the game.

Arlene's second fall was a little more out of the ordinary and occurred at night. Shortly after our arrival in Mexico, friends of friends once removed invited us to their house for dinner. Because we were new to the area and they lived on a steep hill where we imagined finding a parking spot would be like finding a winning lottery ticket, we took a taxi to their house. We dressed up for the occasion, which, for me, meant something other than jeans. Arlene, on the other hand, dressed more up than I, had topped off her outfit with a Mexican shawl, a *rebozo*.

Our hosts lived on a hard-to-find street and even our driver took a few wrong turns. The night was dark, the streets not well-lit. You know the drill.

When we arrived, Arlene opened her backseat door and promptly fell out of the cab, her *rebozo* entangled with the loose-fitting seat belt that had tripped her. As she fell to the ground, she struggled furiously with the seat belt straps looking like the Greek statue of Laocoön and his sons wrestling giant sea serpents. I tried to rush out my door but the door wouldn't open, so, instead, I scooted out Arlene's side, where I, too, fell into the heap that was part-Arlene and part-seatbelt. The taxi driver rushed to our rescue while apologizing loudly for the accident. I'm not sure if he uttered "*¡Ay, carumba!*" or "*¡Ay, chihuahua!*" but I know he said "Ay" several times and followed it with a single word. His mortification was palpable. He untangled us and helped Arlene to her feet, apologized, apologized again, and apologized several more times before going on his way. Arlene sustained a few cuts, a couple of bruises and a slight limp, most of which disappeared with the morning sun. That was Arlene's second fall.

Proving three's the charm, it was on Arlene's third fall that we made our first trip to the local hospital's emergency room. Arlene had been volunteering every Sunday for a fund-raiser known as the Home and Garden Tour, where two or three spectacular houses, a different set each week, are open for public tour for a small fee. Arlene's role on this particular day was to help direct a safe flow of people through a house, telling visitors, "You can't go there," or "You've already seen that room" or "Hey, don't use the bathroom." At the end of the day's tour, she fell. There's no other way to put it. If the sons and daughters of cobblers go shoeless in the streets, then it is only fair to assume the woman who ensures safe walking on a tour would trip and fall. Several people rushed to Arlene's aid, but this time her fall was more serious and, to make matters worse, I wasn't there to help. When she arrived home in a taxi, she was in much pain. So, off to the nearest hospital we went. An x-ray, one wrapped ankle, a private consultation with the emergency room physician and a prescription for a pain killer later, we were on our way home.

I've heard expats talk about the miracle of living in San Miguel, referring to the many opportunities for spiritual growth in this beautiful, historic town rising more than 6,200 feet above sea level, surrounded by hills and draped in sunshine. I know this will come as a shock since I write much bigger, but I am a short man. I simply cannot afford to spend any time growing spiritually when there's still so much physical growth remaining. And let's face it, there's very little that's spiritual about falling on your face in public, especially when sober. But when you fall in the street in San Miguel — and you will fall — there's always someone there to pick you up. That's the real miracle of living here.

A published cartoonist, produced playwright, and award-winning screenwriter, Mark Saunders recently lived in San Miguel for two years with his wife, Arlene

Krasner. Say How's the Foot? *is an excerpt from his humorous account of their experiences. While residing in San Miguel, Mark created* Más o Menos, *a weekly cartoon about expat life, for* Atención, *the city's popular bi-lingual newspaper. More than 500 of his cartoons have appeared in magazines and newspapers, including* The Saturday Evening Post *and the* San Jose Mercury News. *His plays have been performed in regional theatres across America, including in New York City. Two of his short comedies (*Who's on Faust? *&* Playthings*) appear in 2007* The Best Ten-Minute Plays for Three or More Actors, *published by Smith and Kraus.*

Santa Julia Girls

KRISTINE SCHERBER

"¡*Que precioso*!" exclaimed Piedad as she cradled the brown eyed doll in her arms.

"Come along now, we've shopping to do. Don't you want some nice new jeans?" asked Patti.

The warm December sun shone on the table of *navideños*. Tinsel, moss, tiny sheep, miniature cows, shepherds, wise men mounted on camels, and the holy couple all glittering as if they were sprinkled with pixie dust. Wooden *crèches*, hay, Christmas lights and even the devil were arranged on the narrow table tempting holiday shoppers. The proprietor, a handsome curly haired man of thirty, smiled as "our" girls sauntered by, excited by the promise of new shoes, jeans and cute tops.

"That's the first emotion I've seen from her," whispered Patti. "I was beginning to wonder."

Patti, Helen and I were at the San Juan de Dios marketplace with our Santa Julia girls — girls whose home circumstances were horrific. Whether due to abuse, poverty or neglect, these girls were unable to live with their own families. Miriam, Piedad and Paloma were, instead, cared for by the *madres* of the Santa Julia Orphanage, where they would stay for two years before returning home. The nuns provide respite care for forty five girls funded by donations, prayers, and miracles.

Today's outing, initiated by "Backpack Bob," is simple. Give each girl a brand new backpack filled with school supplies and 500 pesos (about $50 US). Each girl may spend it any way she likes. Rather than the endless parade of hand-me-downs, the girls can choose their own outfits. They will learn how to make a bargain, spend money wisely and buy quality garments while feeling empowered to make their own choices.

They are eleven year olds scrubbed clean with unblemished skin, gorgeous black hair pulled back into pony tails, neatly dressed in clothing that almost fits. Miriam was dressed in khaki pants hemmed a bit too short and a black, slightly pilled sweater. Paloma, the fashionista of the group, wore a cream-colored corduroy frock coat, black slacks and looked chic even though she was constantly sucking on a lollipop. Piedad looked much younger than her eleven years, smaller, malnourished, emotionally traumatized. We were three eleven year old girls clothes-shopping with three middle aged gringas.

We entered the market with confused trepidation. Miriam headed right for the shoes. Smiling, she modeled her first choice, black patent leather flats with a pink and black plaid bow on the toe box. "*Que piensa, Señora?*" She gazed up confidently, her soft brown eyes seeking my approval. I gave them a thumbs up and wondered if they had them in my size.

"Yes, Miriam, you may buy them. Now we have just 420 pesos remaining." I used my best Spanish and my best motherly tone. I explained to the shop keeper that these are Santa Julia girls, all three of them, may we have a discount? She smiled and granted us fifteen percent.

Despite the language barrier, age and cultural differences, we enjoyed spending the day together. The market, known for its stunning array of inexpensive flowers, was crowded with families shopping for gifts, food, clothing, and decorations for Christmas. Six-pointed star-shaped *piñatas* covered with red, blue, orange, pink and green crepe paper streamers twisted in the breeze above our heads. The scent of fresh pine boughs mingled with the strong aroma of green chili chicken *tamales* steamed and sold from an aluminum push cart. An older woman sat on a low stool stroking a live chicken and gazed vacantly at the crowd. Children tugged at their parents, pulling them toward toys to be delivered by the Three Kings on January 6th.

After purchasing a pink fuzzy coat with matching beret for Piedad, sparkle-pocket jeans for Paloma and Miriam and new tennis shoes for all, we left the cramped, narrow aisles of the market and emerged into a brilliant blue day.

Leaving the way we had come, Piedad stopped and the entrance and reached for a brown-eyed baby doll.

"Would you like him, honey?" asked Patti. "I think I have some extra money."

Piedad grinned. The other girls crowded the counter examining the beautifully hand-knitted doll clothing. Soft dresses, booties, blankets and tiny socks in blue, yellow, green and white angora yarn begged to be touched, fondled, snuggled.

"Let's buy one for each girl," suggested Helen. "They have so little."

Pleased, the shopkeeper removed the doll clothing from its protective plastic wrapper and the girls began to dress their babies. Golden gladiator sandals completed the color-coordinated ensembles and each girl searched for the perfect blanket to swaddle her treasure for the trip back. With infinite patience and true enjoyment, the proprietor joined the fun, jamming tiny limbs into small sleeves, buckling sandals and even suggesting the need for *ropa interior* (underwear) which Miriam just had to have for her doll. Piedad, elated, eyes shining, mumbled her thanks to all of us for this privilege.

"What are you going to name your baby?" asked Patti.

Startled by the question, Piedad looked deeply into Patti's British blue eyes and answered her question. "Why, he is the Baby Jesus, the Son of God."

While we gathered our purchases, each of the Santa Julia girls tenderly carried her Baby Jesus back to the orphanage where, according to Mexican tradition, he will be placed in a manger on Christmas Eve.

After a 35-year career spanning ministry to medicine, Kristine ditched the cell phone, pager and brutal call schedule of a Minneapolis cardiac hospital for the mountains of San Miguel de Allende. Here she lives full time with her husband, John, and SPA Shelter rescue dog, Brownie. She spends her time reading, gardening, studying Spanish, creating a unique line of jewelry, and hiking the gorgeous canyons of Mexico. Kristine and her husband fund a private charity giving school scholarships to neighborhood children.

Bienvenido a San Miguel o ¿Ya Mero?

RUTH KEAR

"Sending my angels along with you for the border crossing. If they don't do the trick then at least you'll get a good story out of it! Oh, and remember to laugh..."

My friend's words echoed in my mind all the way from Denver to San Miguel. Her angels did in fact do a fabulous job getting us across the border. Rocinante, the silver Rav4 loaded inside and out, breezed through five military check points and four *aduana* stations without a hitch. No crooked cops and no *morditas*.

On the last leg of the trip, just as the sun was beginning to set, we reached the outskirts of San Luis Potosi. This would be the last night that we would have to sneak the cat kennels into a hotel.

"Start looking for a likely place," said C. *Likely* meaning a motel with exterior doors so we could just back into a parking space and discreetly throw a towel over the kennels as we sneaked in the door.

"You know..." I began.

C looked at me with a knowing glance.

"OK, he replied," as he edged over to the right lane with the overhead sign stating, "San Miguel Allende 197 km." "But you know what they say about driving in Mexico at night."

"Hey," I said, "we've got our angels, remember?"

As the last rays of crimson sank below the horizon, streaks of lightning illuminated the sky in the direction of San Miguel and the wind rattled through the overloaded roof rack. Ten minutes into the drive, rain began to batter the windshield.

Highway 57 south to Querétaro is an excellent four-lane highway that is a main north and south artery...in other words, it is a truck route. The tail lights of the double *semi-remolque* trailers whip-lashed across the rain-slick highway.

"Guess I forgot about it being the rainy season," I mumbled as I checked to make sure my seat belt was fastened.

"Yeah," said C. "Let's just hope there aren't any animals on the road."

He had no sooner gotten the words out, when the truck in front of us swerved wildly as a vaquero appeared on the edge of the highway astride a horse with two burros following behind.

"Jeez," that was close," breathed C as he gripped the steering wheel a little tighter.

"I guess mañana doesn't apply to driving," I commented.

There was an audible sigh of relief from both of us when we finally saw the turn off for Los Rodriguez and San Miguel.

"We're almost home," I said. It was still raining.

The road to our *casita* was unmarked, but we knew it was the same turn-off to San Jose de Amistad so how could we have both missed it? It was late and we were hungry, tired, and ready for a shower. And now we were getting cranky. The *terraceria* was filled with deep puddles and rocks and I couldn't seem to control my need to advise C to be careful.

We finally arrived at the entrance to the driveway. Through the pouring rain the headlights glinted off a newly installed metal gate complete with chain and padlock.

"Call Salo," I said. Salo was our *contratista* who lived nearby.

"It's 1 am," growled C, "we can't call Salo."

Reluctantly, we dragged ourselves out of the car into the unabated rain. C grabbed the flashlight from the glove box and we each took a cat kennel and crawled through the fence adjacent to the stone wall, the barbwire tearing at our clothes. We stumbled through the wet grass, the cat claw bushes scratching our bare legs while the real cats yowled as if the world were coming to an end.

"Let's hope there's electricity," said C as the door to the *casita* swung open.

"*Gracias por dios,*" I said as the lights flicked on.

It took our eyes a few seconds to adjust to the brightness. We saw the vacant space next to the stove at the same time.

"Where the hell is the refrigerator?" asked C.

I saw that the window over the kitchen sink was broken and the screen ripped out. There were traces of something that looked like bird shit on the window ledge and more of the same on the tile floor.

I took a deep breath. "Surely Salo would have told us if someone had ripped off our refrigerator, maybe there was a problem and he..." I said, my voice trailing off.

"I don't want to analyze it now. I just want to go to bed," said C pulling back the comforter.

"What about a hot shower?"

"In the morning," snapped C as he climbed into bed.

We awakened at 6:30 the next morning by sun streaming through the curtainless window. I threw a blanket over the window and bumbled back to bed...to no avail. The construction crew had arrived and the *ranchera* music was blaring. I heard a scratching sound at the door and opened it. It was the welcome committee: three Mexican ranch dogs greeted me with toothy smiles and wagging tails

"God, what next?" snarled C from under the pillow.

"C'mon', lighten up. Let's make the best of it. We are finally here, safe and sound. And now I'm going to figure out how to make some coffee while you shower."

"OK," I guess a hot shower would feel great," said C disappearing into the bathroom.

I located a bag of coffee in the cupboard and a couple of bottles of water under the sink. As I fashioned a filter out of a paper towel, C yelled, "Jeezus, there's no hot water, turn on the stove and see if it lights."

I clicked on the burner. *Nada.*

"Crap, crap and more crap," yelled C. "Go check the propane tank."

The needle on the tank was so far into empty I could barely see it. I walked back into the *casita* and we both plopped down on the bed.

I handed C a cup of the stale tasting coffee.

"Yuck," he said, taking a sip. "Why didn't Salo tell us that the refrigerator had been stolen? He knew when we were coming."

"Maybe it just happened," I said.

There was a knock at the door and we both jumped.

"*Hola*, it's Salo. *Bienvenidos a México*. How was your trip?"

Salo kissed me on both cheeks and gave C a warm *abrazo*. How could we be grumps with such a warm welcome?

The robbery had happened a month before our arrival. Salo had not discovered it for several days because it had been raining and the crew had not been working. So, when they finally made the discovery, the door had been left open for a while and birds had flown inside and roosted on the window ledge. He hadn't told us because he wanted us to see what had happened. Hmm...another deep breath. I tried to think like a Mexican. My *gringa* mind was saying, he's known when we were coming for months and that a fridge would be real handy and why in the hell didn't he tell me so that I could go and have him buy me another one???? Deep breath and a big smile.

"Is anything else missing?" he asked.

I looked around the room and remembered that I had left an old Beacon blanket at the foot of the bed. It was gone. Oh well, winter was coming and they probably needed it more than we did.

"They drank your tequila too," Salo remarked. "But I washed the glasses and put everything away." Apparently after their heist the robbers had relaxed in the sala drinking a bottle of Don Julio to celebrate! But, on the bright side, nothing else had been taken, nor had the place been ransacked. Classy *hombres,* I thought.

I tuned back into the conversation to hear Salo telling C that he had arranged for the alarm folks to come and install a system.

Oh my god! I had avoided an alarm system my entire life in the US and now here I was in *el campo* in Mexico with a screaming alarm! Several gulps of air. How much is this going to cost, I wonder, my brain whirring with thoughts of my dwindling pesos.

"OK," I said to C after Salo left. "Here are our orders of the day: call for propane delivery, get money to buy a new refrigerator...*efectivo* (cash)...you can get a better deal and we might as well begin our adjustment to a cash economy."

We found a fridge in the scratch-and-dent section of the local appliance vendor. They could deliver it today, no charge. Ah yes, now I was beginning to remember why I loved it here. Way out in the outback, down a bumpy, muddy and rutted road and there is no charge for delivery. They arrived two hours later, nary a complaint about the road. With an extra measure of aplomb, they placed the new Mabe in the empty space. C gave the young men a generous tip for all their troubles. They grinned ear to ear and said in synchronization, "*A sus ordenes...*Señor."

C was planning to fly back to Colorado at the end of the week. I would be on my own until the house was finished, *ojalá*, in February or March. Since the house was my "swan song" after a 30-year career in restaurant design, I would be the one to live in the tiny *casita* for the next six months. The stress of building a home in the US was difficult enough and we couldn't fathom what surprises we would encounter in Mexico.

The afternoon that C was to leave, I took him to the Mega parking lot to catch the shuttle to Leon. I wasn't feeling comfortable enough to make the drive to the airport and back alone.

"See you in December," said C kissing me goodbye. "*Buena suerte.*"

"Yeah," I said, giving him a hug. "I'll probably need it."

Inside Mega, I wandered up and down the aisles looking for spices, toilet paper, cleaning supplies and all the other accouterments one needs when setting up house. I came out with a cart full of stuff. Another peso or two was for the elderly woman who helped me load my groceries into the back of the car. I was beginning to feel settled.

I got into the car and turned the key. Click, click. I tried several times until even the click wasn't audible. Oh no! I thought. I should have gotten that cell phone before C left. I locked the car and went back into the store to call Salo. He answered on the first ring. I scribbled the directions to his mechanic and thanked god that I had not bought any ice cream.

"Can you get the car to the mechanic?" he asked. "I can't come to help you for a while."

"I'll buy some jumper cables," I said. "I think it's just the battery."

In the parking lot, I smiled my *gringa* smile and a nice young man came to my aid. Ten minutes later, I pulled into the mechanic's shop where a genial man with a big smile and a warm handshake greeted me.

"*Sí, Señora, sí, se puede,*" he said when I asked him if he could replace the battery in my car. An hour later and another $1150 pesos paid, I drove back up the Caracol to our *casita*.

I put the groceries away and fell into bed exhausted. And then the barking began. I opened the door and shouted at the dogs to be quiet. There is nothing for them to be barking about...or is there? Maybe it's the wind rustling through the rebar protruding up through the walls of the house or are they answering calls of dogs a mile away in San Jose de Amistad? I didn't sleep a wink.

The next morning, I discovered the gnawed and shredded remains of plastic bags and bottles left by the construction crew strewn all over the porch and yard. Looks like the dogs are still in the oral stage, I mused.

When I mentioned the events of the previous night to Salo, he told me that I must yell, "*Órale!*" and throw rocks at them so they will go home. Hmmm. Deep breath. I had never thrown a rock at an animal in my life so I figured that I had probably inherited these pups. Our poor cats may never go outside again.

Getting a cell phone and Internet service in Mexico is like buying a house NOB. This is not an exaggeration. I went to the recommended ISP cellular provider on Wednesday at 2 pm. I was there until 7:30 pm and I left with nothing.

"Come back tomorrow at 10 am with all your documents (passport, utility bill, etc.) and we can do it quickly," said Dee with a smile.

I arrived at the specified time and filled out same documents that I had filled out the day before.

"We need to wait for paperwork back from the home office in Mexico City, 10-15 minutes," said Dee and she suggested that I go get a coffee.

I wandered around Luciernaga Mall for 30 minutes before returning to the store.

"Not yet," said Dee, shaking her head. "Maybe you should have lunch and then come back."

When I returned at 3 pm, Dee had gone to dinner and her associate told me that maybe tomorrow first thing. But why can't they give me a reason for the delay, I thought as I drove home. I was beginning to get paranoid.

Friday morning. I pinned on a big smile and headed back to IUSA cell. I just knew by the end of the day I would have a cell phone and Internet. I greeted Dee who asked for all my documents *again*. There seemed to be a problem with my *dirección* (address). My utility bill said, "*Cerrada 7*" but my official paperwork said, "*Privada 7.*"

"What is the difference?" I asked.

"*Nada, son igual.*" "Nothing, it's the same."

And the problem is???

"One government office says one thing and the other says something else. This is always a problem here in Mexico," she opined. "But we can do it now. Except now you have to register your cell phone with the Mexican government or it won't work."

"OK," I said, "let's do it."

"But Señora, you do not have a Mexican social security card with a number."

Oh my god!

"No problem, you can use mine," she said.

"*¿En serio?*" I asked incredulously. "OK," I murmured, silently hoping that her boyfriend wasn't involved with any *narcotráficos*.

Two hours later, I walked out with my new cell phone and BAM...*Banda Ancha Movil.* All instructions for usage were in in Spanish. "Ha, ha, ha" I laughed, when Dee asked me if I needed any help setting up my phone. "*Es mi tarea.*"

When I arrived back at the *casita*, I discovered an envelope had been slipped under the door. I turned it over noting the US and Mexican post marks almost two weeks earlier. I recalled that I had emailed all my friends my Mexican address with a little note saying that it looked good even if it wasn't really functional as there is no mail delivery in this part of the *campo*. I get my utility bill out of a cardboard box that sits on the counter in the little *tienda* in the village near me. Apparently one of my friends had decided to send me a card via "snail mail". I went outside and asked the construction crew if they had seen anyone delivering mail to my *casit*a. "*No Señora, no hay servicio de correo aqui.*"

"*Pero, yo recibí una tarjeta,*" I said. They just smiled and shook their heads in disbelief.

I had the phone up and running after only a few glitches. Feeling very smug, I hooked up BAM. *Nada, nada, absolutamente nad*a. Yikes, I had already signed a contract. Will I have to go back and hassle again if the service doesn't work out here in *el campo*?

I didn't want to think anymore about the looming challenge of mañana. I turned on some tunes, opened the fridge, grabbed a cold one and went outside, the screen door banging behind me. The pups joined me on the steps, their slender bodies waggling with delight. As I took a long cold swallow of beer and watched another glorious sunset begin to form, I contemplated the mystery of the card delivery. Mañana, I thought, mañana. Isn't that why I came here? *Ya Mero*...almost ready, almost done, almost there, almost....

Although Ruth Kear is a recent jubilada to San Miguel de Allende, she has traveled extensively throughout Mexico for many years. Ruth's love affair with Mexico began in the early 60's and grew over the years as her career in restaurant design and architecture brought her to Mexico many times to research Mexican architectural design and search for artifacts for her restaurant clients. In 2009 she decided it was time to design her "swan song," a Mexican style home in the campo outside San Miguel. In her cozy studio overlooking the Picacho Mountains she looks forward to many more years documenting the wonderful life experiences she has always had in Mexico.

A Painter's Day of Color in San Miguel de Allende

JUDITH JENYA

S unlight on bright fuchsia bougainvillea, fire engine red geraniums color the morning.

Soft green silver spikes of aloe, dark grayish green cactus, delicate buttercup flowers with tiny alizarin tendrils appear beneath the yellow and black of a buzzing bee.

Pomegranates red and light green hang from trees with deep green leaves; lemon trees reaching toward an azure sky filled with puffy white clouds.

Ochre cement sides, windowpanes of violet abut mustard colored walls trimmed in mauve, red tiles on the roof. Its neighbor boasts sky blue gates, a mango orange door, on top raw umber with burnt orange flaking paint.

Burnt cinnamon colored door opens to a restaurant, its tables spread with a watermelon red cloth with white squares, pale yellow napkins, chairs of cucumber green and china blue sit on floors of rust colored tiles.

Shawls hang in parrot like colors cadmium yellow, orange, red, lilac blue, green and white in *tiendas* where baskets of straw are filled with dried flowers turning cream white and brown as they dry.

Fountains of faded red cement turning papaya color splash at corners where soft brown, gray, ivory cobblestones meet.

Women wearing dresses of royal purple with cream and Christmas-red trim, canary green aprons, their raven colored braids woven with pearl ribbons carry babies in blankets of soft pink or wrapped tightly in *rebozos* of blue black and gray stripes.

Green and white taxis, light blue and white clad mounted policemen at the corner of el jardín with the pink, ecru and soft beige/gray of La Parroquia behind them and in front, balloons of every color make a rainbow outlined in the cerulean sky.

Sunset brings a horizon of coral, rose, eggshell pink, and pale yellow as dancing water on the cobblestones reflect silver clouds tinged with light gold shimmering in the heavens,

Spiral rocket fireworks, iridescent colors arch across the firmament. Threads of silver lights exploding irises, yellow, violet, copper colored stems linger beneath snakes hissing orange fire, lily white cut shapes illuminate the dark. Deep sea blue night sky with a brazen moon of yellow gold its penumbra glistening from behind feathery clouds lights chocolate shadows awaiting the dawn.

Un día de color para una pintora en San Miguel de Allende.

Mañana

La brillante bugambilia fucshia enciende el fuego de los geranios rojos. El verde grisáceo de la sávila apunta delicadas flores en el verde oscuro del nopal. Pequeñas enredaderas negras y amarillas suben como abejas zumbantes. Están ahí las rojas granadas y el verde claro del limonero. El cielo acaricia el blanco de las nubes con su azur. Un cemento ocre al lado de una ventana violeta con vidrio mostaza colorea las paredes lilas acomodando las tejas del techo. Aquel puente azul cobalto lleva a una puerta color mango en cuyo crudo y umbrío tope flamea descascarada la pintura.

Tarde

La quemante canela da color a la puerta del restaurante donde se ven los manteles de sandías, las servilletas amarillas, el verde de los pepinos y las rústicas sillas azul china coloreando el piso de azulejo. Las plumas del loro relumbran en los rebozos amarillos, anaranjados, rojos, lilas y blancos que hay en la tienda junto a las canastas tejidas con flores secas que se vuelven poco a poco blancas, beiges, cafés. Las fuentes palidecen frente al rojo cemento y el color de la papaya salpica las esquinas donde el suave café y el gris marfil de los guijarros se encuentran.

Las mujeres traen sus vestidos púrpura, crema y rojo navideño surgiendo bajo los mandiles que recuerdan el verde de la manzana. Sus trenzas tan negras como cuervos están ahora coloreadas y tejidas con listones color perla; ellas cargan sus bebés en sábanas rosa pálido o en rebozos con rayas grises, azules y negras.

Pasan taxis verdes con blanco. Policías montados uniformados con blanco y azul claro. Las bancas del jardín lucen el negro brillante. Mientras la Parroquia y su rosa y suave beige. Contrasta con globos de todos los colores del arco iris.

En el horizonte el atardecer juega entre corales, rosas suaves y amarillos que palidecen. El agua danza en los guijarros reflejando las nubes de plata y destellos dorados tiñen brillos en el cielo añil.

Noche

Fuegos de artificio forman cohetes de iridiscentes colores. Luces como hilos de plata explotan en amarillos y violetas; vapores cobrizos coloreados formando serpientes que sisean el fuego anaranjado. El blanco de los lirios corta formas iluminadas en la oscuridad.

El azul navío hace brasa con la luna dorada y amarilla, su penumbra reluce detrás de nubes como plumas que iluminan las sombras esperando el amanecer.

— *Translated by Eugenia Yllades*

Judith Jenya is a poet, painter, photographer and memoir writer, living in San Miguel for the past four years. Her short story, Dubrovnik Afternoon, *was published in the* Hamilton Stone *online literary magazine. Judith has read at many literary events. She lived in California for much of her life, mainly in the Bay area. She attended UC Berkeley for her BA and MSW and she taught there. She raised her daughter and son on Oahu where she lived for 20 years, working as an art and family therapist, and as an attorney specializing in adoptions. She founded and directed Global Children's Organization providing healing and restoration to children from all sides of the wars in the Balkans, and Northern Ireland. Her artistic and professional life have been peripatetic, allowing her to visit all the continents and work in many countries.*

Celebration

IRENE WENDE

The woman in front of me was unmistakably "dead" so how could I be so entranced with her? God knows it wasn't the face. But if, one could fall for attitude, then she had it in spades — it poured out of her skeletal frame. I reached out to touch her, but stopped half-way. Embarrassed, I looked around the store. The "woman" was actually a life-size reproduction — a skeletal creation of someone's ingenious hand. I looked at the others on the shelf beside her, miniature imitations of the five foot model before me. And then I looked back at *her*. The body language — ooo la la. The lady *was* showing a lot of leg considering the dress she wore. It covered her from her neck to her toes and the bony leg protruding through the slit from the front of her dress was anything but well, demure. But it was her face, the hollow eyes, the bulging teeth, and the grin; *that* grin. It was enough to scare any man, dead or alive. It got your attention. But, for some reason, she chose to keep it visible, and the wide hat she wore accentuated, rather than hid, the grotesque face. It was almost as if she wanted to make sure *you* noticed her. And it worked. I couldn't keep my eyes off her.

I was standing in one of the many shops of San Miguel. I turned around to look for my friend, Gaby, and found her watching me with amused eyes. "So, it is true, yes? Beauty *is* in the eye of the beholder. This lady, at least, will be happy to know. It is good you are single, yes? A wife would be very jealous if she saw you looking at a woman like that." She slapped me on the back. "Poor Carl, so which one will you chose?"

The tall "lady" was not for sale. I walked to a shelf and picked up one of the smaller figures. I turned her around and looked for the price tag. Two hundred and twenty nine pesos. Not bad for someone of her background.

I looked at Gaby. "Okay, I admit it. There's something about her. So, who is she?"

This was my second day here and it seemed that every store was carrying the figures. Except for the one in front of me, most of them were miniatures. She was the first life size one I had seen. "I don't have to wonder what she is thinking. It's all there in her face, her stance. She is definitely high class. How did the artist create something so perfect?"

Gaby looked at me, surprised. "You mean, imperfect, don't you?"

"No. I mean perfect. She *is* perfect in her own way."

Gaby laughed. "I wonder who would appreciate the compliment more? The artist or Catrina?"

"Is that her name?"

She nodded. "You are looking at Catrina. She is part of *el* Dia de los Muertos. Come, I will show you. We will walk to the *jardín*, the square, after we make our purchases. Next week is the Day of the Dead Celebration. On the first and second of November."

"And what about October thirty first?"

"Ah, Halloween. No, this is not the same. Halloween is a different tradition. Catrina was created by the Mexican illustrator, Jose Guadalupe Posada." And she smiled. "But, my friend, she is not what you think she is." She pointed to the small Catrina I was holding. "You see the clothes she wears? She is very elegant; the broad brimmed hats, the shoes, the fancy clothes This was the upper class of the 1900's in Mexico."

"But why the skeletal face?"

"It is very effective, yes? It was how Posada wanted to show the social inequalities and injustices in Mexico between the rich and the poor. He worked for many newspapers and made many drawings with *calaveras*, skeletons, and images of death to show this. And not only women *calaveras*, but men too. I think you call it black humor, yes?'

I nodded and she continued. "Many Mexicans could not read, but political and, what do you call it, satirical, yes, satirical drawings with skeletons are something we can all understand. Better than words, yes? He wanted to show that we are all the same regardless of wealth or status. His work was very popular."

"So, Catrina is mocking the living through death."

She nodded. "*Sí*, all of us are mortal." And then she laughed. "But do not worry. You will be able to see many Catrinas later. Live Catrinas. There will be a parade and many women will dress as Catrina. So, you will not be disappointed.'

"But how does Catrina fit into the festival?"

"She is a new part of the celebration in San Miguel. We like to party here. It is another opportunity to dress up in beautiful costumes and enjoy ourselves." She looked at the Catrina in my hand. "So, you have chosen one? Come, let us pay and then we will go to the *jardín*".

There was no use walking beside Gaby; there wasn't enough room on the narrow, cobbled sidewalks and streets,. I followed behind her, trying to avoid the cars and people coming from all directions. The city was stunning and I caught glimpses of the beautiful, warm pastel colors of the buildings as we maneuvered our way to the *jardín*. I smiled as Gaby greeted a friend with a big hug and an even bigger smile.

Suddenly, she stopped, turned around and grabbed my arm. "Listen! Do you hear that? The music? The laughing? The talking? It is life *and* death celebrated together. Come, I will show you." She pulled me into the square. "You see this altar? You see these photos? These are the photos of those who are no longer with us. And this? All the beautiful flowers laid out like a carpet? And the smell of the *copal*, the incense? The light from the candles? The smell of the foods? The colors of the *papeles*, the cutouts? These are all here to help guide the deceased soul back home. Later, the food is shared by family and friends and, for a short time, they are together again.

"Is that beer on the altar?" There were other odd things too. Trinkets, jewelry, and plates of food, all surrounded by tiny skulls. I moved closer and touched one. It was soft and made of sugar. I looked around the square, filled with people and altars. I thought of the small, private, quiet ceremonies back home. "Are the displays always so public?"

Gaby laughed. "This is a public celebration to honor those who have done much for San Miguel and Mexico. But at home it is much more private and families and friends decorate altars for their loved ones who have passed. The altars hold many of the things they enjoyed during their life.

"And then there is the celebration at the *panteón*, the cemetery. Families stay all day and bring favorite possessions of their loved ones, and wash and decorate the graves. They bring *copal* and candles, and more food and flowers,. They eat and sing and pray and talk to their loved ones."

"I've never seen death celebrated with so much living," I said. Why do we treat death with so much sadness back home? I struggled for the right word.

"It's so alive here. You do all this to bring the dead back?"

"*Sí.* It is also to sustain them in the afterlife. The aromas, the smells feed the souls until the next year when they come again. But, you must also look at it from the point of view of the dead."

She stretched out her arms again. "Look at all this. How can they not come back? Their loved ones are calling them. They entice them with the things that they loved on earth." She grabbed me by the arm again. "Come. You see this altar?" She pointed to the photo of a deceased man. "That man likes good food and tequila." We walked to the one next to it. "And this person likes enchiladas and Coca-Cola. And here are some of the things that gave him great comfort and joy in his life, a favorite CD, his shoes, and, look, a straw hat. Each year, they are put on the alter. It does not matter if we are rich, or famous, or poor. We are all vain. Who does not want the opportunity to come back?." She laughed that delectable laugh that comes from being able to laugh at one's self. She looked at me. "Come, let us sit down and have something to drink."

We walked to one of the cafés surrounding the *jardín* and sat down at a table. A waiter took our order and we settled into our chairs; comfortable and relaxed. The word "alive" kept swirling through my head. I looked into the square. Children played amongst the alters, vendors sold roasted corn and dogs were chased after balloons. Everywhere people, sitting and talking in the park, on benches, on the steps, and in the cafés.

I wondered what the Mexicans thought of all the tourists pointing and staring at the altars. And did the tourists find the openness intimidating or welcoming? Were they thinking of someone left behind, someone they wished could be here to see life and death celebrated together?

And then I thought of Tim, my brother, and of the cemetery where he lay, of our last conversation just before he died, holding his hand and wishing there was some way to stop the helplessness I had felt. Trying to tell him the things I wished I had told him before, the things I still had in my head. I thought of the sadness and loss I felt on the last anniversary of his death, holding onto the bouquet of flowers and staring down at the small, gray, flat stone with his name. Trying to keep him alive, trying to remember him and realizing I was forgetting. Three years.

I blinked and looked again at the altars in the square soaring up towards the sky, calling out. I imagined the souls moving through the gentle rolling hills of San Miguel, returning home. And something stirred inside me.

I felt Gaby squeeze my hand. Our drinks had arrived. I watched the waiter pour the beer into the tall glasses and I remembered that Tim liked beer. And peanuts and chips. And t-shirts and loud music. I sat up straight in my chair. Images tugged at me. I remembered the box at home. The box with Tim's name on it. I couldn't remember what was in it, only that it held things I hadn't been able to let go of, things that belonged to Tim, things that Tim had loved. I could make an altar. I could put all his favorite things on it. I could tell him about San Miguel. About Catrina. And everything else that I had wanted to tell him and hadn't.

I could still feel Gaby holding my hand. Quiet, understanding. I squeezed her hand. She had invited me to San Miguel; had told me that late October would be a good time to visit. She had known.

I looked at her. "I think when I get back home I will visit my brother."

"Ah." She smiled. "And will you bring him something from San Miguel?"

I nodded. "I think he will like the skeletons." We smiled at each other. We both knew that I was talking about something else. And I added, "I can tell him about today."

We raised our glasses and made a toast. "To our loved ones."

Irene was born in Canada where after a 29 year successful career in banking she decided to change careers and incorporate her love of traveling with something new—teaching English to international students. For the last six years she has been teaching English as an ESL Instructor in various parts of the world: Canada, Brazil, the Czech Republic, and Mexico. She loves the challenge of discovery and possibilities...not only for herself but for her students. And now change is in the air again: she is pursuing another creative venue: writing. She feels life is indeed a celebration!

Gringo Haiku Redux

Lulu Torbet and Leah Feldon

hen we wrote *Gringo Haiku* two years ago, we thought we'd pretty much summed up ex-pat life in San Miguel in easy-to-digest seventeen-syllable verses. But times, and San Miguel, keep on changing. So we're back, we women of few words, with more succinct observations on local life and lifestyle that will help you enjoy our beloved pueblo.

To review briefly: Haiku is an ancient, venerated Japanese verse form, consisting of seventeen syllables in lines of five, seven, and five syllables. Gringo Haiku is a shamelessly irreverent perversion of the traditional form, yet is somehow uniquely appropriate to the quality of ex-pat life here. For one thing, we're always in a hurry; even a fourteen line sonnet is too long. Also, the stench of the *arroyos* evokes a somewhat different reaction than the scent of plum blossoms. Thus, the elevated "Aha!" moment of the best Japanese haiku can more often be translated here as "*¡Ay, caramba!*" or "Oy vey!"

Certainly "*Ay caramba*" moments are a peso a dozen in San Miguel. There are more big new stores, sprawling developments, traffic jams, and mystifying street detours than ever before. There's even (gasp!) a Starbucks on the square. But we're not complaining here, just reporting. And we take pride in San Miguel's burgeoning interest in sustainability, organic food, green building, and recycling.

There are other points worth noting: Our research shows — and we have looked at these issues closely — that 2 x 1 drinks are available everywhere. That the guy who rubber stamps the paperwork at Immigration can now do 54.5 copies a minute. That the chances of getting caught in a drenching downpour are inversely proportionate to the number of flimsy plastic bags you are carrying. That everyone talks about taking it easier, but is in fact is busier than ever. That a comfortable couch is still hard to find. That a rumor originating in Guadiana will make its way to Guadalupe in less than twenty minutes, but with the facts *ever so slightly* distorted. That new restaurants open at the rate of one per day, and close at the rate of .8 per day, leaving a net gain of .2 restaurants per day, for an increase of 73 new restaurants per year, serving the cuisine of approximately 49 nations.

All said, we are delighted to live here. Think of *Gringo Haiku Redux* as an insider's update on *la vida* local, bulletins on the latest trends, synopses of customs and mores, unsolicited tips and advice, and random sound bytes that attempt to illuminate the inexplicable.

Cars prowl the mean streets
in search of the holy grail:
A parking space.

What's up with this weird
confluence of men sporting
long gray ponytails?

La Parroquia:
A luscious brightly lit cake
good enough to eat.

Senior brain struggles
to learn Spanish. Hear today
but gone tomorrow.

Ahorita. The
quintessential unit
of Mexican time.

Five-year residents
down tequila straight up and
mourn the good old days

The true disaster:
Swine flu drubs economy.
Aporkalyse now!

Steamy tango, hot
salsa moves. Shake your booty
at...*Arthur Murray* ??

SMA chat rooms:
Rumors, insults, spats. C'mon,
you call this Civil?

Maestro, albanil,
cantera, barra. Ex-pat's
first Spanish words.

Smart green homes vie with
grandiose developments.
San Miguel stand-off.

Crossing the border,
car jammed with contraband, I
pray for a green light.

Shopping, *comida,*
then a nice long siesta.
Ex-pat triathlon.

Rain pounds pavements as
downspouts turn streets to rivers.
San Miguel car wash!

Steadfast companions
on our journey: amoebas,
salmonella, worms.

Plan B or not Plan B?
Hamlet ponders fine print of
Medicare options.

Add *habaneros*.
Garnish. Serve without warning.
Mexican hot flash.

Potholes, falling bricks,
loose gratings. Whiplash! Pain! If
only I could sue!

Organic produce,
recycling, solar power.
This is the third world?

Local personal
ad: "Mature woman seeks mate. . .
still breathing a plus."

Scent of jasmine as
dawn breaks through pink-tinged clouds. Then
the hammering starts.

Narcotráficos,
bandidos, carjacks. Big deal.
It's still paradise.

Aurora Art Walk:
Hang out with pals, drink free wine.
And...*oh yeah*, the art.

Lectures, conferences,
workshops, classes. Campus life
at San Miguel U.

Haiku too short to
capture San Miguel mojo.
You've gotta be here.

No long bios for
haiku authors. Visit please
two humble websites:

www.leahfeldon.com
www.lulutorbet.blogspot.com

Two Poems

BRENDA NETTLES RIOJAS

He Translates the Rain

Another day of rain,
no commas, no periods

in this constant pour
that does not deter
us from exploring
the cobblestone city

or venturing into *el jardín*
where the *mariachis* play
under the gazebo past midnight.

Near La Parroquia, soaked, we
find a cab for refuge, for dry.

"Beautiful," says the driver,
a local who captures the city's spark.
"The rain replenishes the water reserves,

it brings us what we need
to drink, to bathe, to live."

"If this was a desert,
we would not be alive today."

His translation modifies
our wet sock complaints.

Letter Left Under the Flower Pot at
Casa de las Guadalupes Donde Juegan Los Colibris

Dear Virgencita Morena, I find you everywhere, painted
on tile, a trivet near the stove. I go outside and you watch
me from the window; later I find you with your hands in
prayer under the sunflowers in the garden.

I carry you in my purse, rosary beads, my ignored devotion. Without entering a church, we bring you roses and
votives for your altar found in every corner here in San
Miguel.

I pass through the market and you stand out, embroidered
with sequins on purses, glittered, stitched, dangled. You
hang from a young girl's earrings. Accompanied by Frida
and La Catrina, your image on sale, printed on shopping
bags, aprons, bracelets, notebooks and boxes. Even the
house cat has your name.

Since you arrived on Tepeyac and left your image on Juan
Diego's *tilma*, you, the muse of poets and artists, my celes-
tial mother. Rusted in tin, carved from pine and *cantera*,
formed from *papier-mâché*, painted on my breakfast and
dinner plate, our prayers silenced in stone.

Virgencita Morena, pray for us.

Brenda Nettles Riojas is a mother, writer, and creative spirit, who grew up on the border of South Texas and Mexico. Brenda is currently working on her MFA in creative writing through the University of New Orleans. She completed three summer residencies in Madrid, Spain (2007), San Miguel de Allende, Mexico (2008), and at the Ezra Pound Center for Literature at Brunnenburg in Merano, Italy. She is the editor and host of Corazón Bilingüe, *an online poetry journal and weekly radio program that explores the dynamics of language, culture and the art of literary creation. Her poetry has been published in a number of anthologies and publications including* di-verse-city, Ribbons, 2008 & 2011 Texas Poetry Calendar, Interstice, Ellipsis, Boundless *and* Ezra - An Online Journal of Translation. *Her most recent collection of poems,* La Primera Voz Que Oí, *was published in Guadalajara, Mexico.*

Picarón

Susan McKinney de Ortega

William cannot figure out what it is about himself that is amiss. He wears tennis shoes and casual shirts like the other students and he carries his English/Spanish dictionary and notebook in the same style of native woven pouch. He shows up early for class and gamely tries to speak a few words of impromptu Spanish with Raul, the teacher, just like the other students do. But there is something he can't put his finger on — something the others know that is out of his reach.

Today Raul is late. William settles himself into a desk. Lord, they were made for 20-year old bodies! He glances around the gathering semicircle. Young Juan is slouched in the blue jeans and white t-shirt he wears every day, looking hung over. *Crudo.* That's a word William remembers, but there are many he does not. Spanish words seem to light on his brain like the Monarch butterflies of Michoacán, and then fly away. Maybe that is why he thinks he catches the others passing amused glances over his head at times, but, then again, maybe that is not the case at all. We have more in common than not, William thinks. We might be different in age, but we are all visitors in central Mexico for a few weeks, a few months, trying to make Spanish easy on our tongues.

The one called Ashley, what a lush beauty she is, William notices. Probably only twenty years old like Juanito, with skin like milk, and brown hair, tangled in the style of the long-haired rasta-folk in Los Angeles. She speaks little. When she does, it's halting, and William feels a special kinship. Ashley comes in and sits at the end of the semicircle. She is wearing flowing Indian-print pants. William gives her a little smile. He would like to know what type of figure Ashley has, but he can't tell because of her oversized clothes. But then she pushes her hair back with a languid arm and William spies a creamy half-moon of tummy. He flips through his Spanish/English dictionary to see if it contains the word "Rubenesque."

Raul comes in flashing grins at everyone. William likes that, in Raul's view, conversational Spanish should be just that: conversational.

When it's Juan's turn to *platicar*, ("chat," a word William remembers, but has a hard time pronouncing) he uses the word *borracho*. Drunk. *Enojado* (angry) is another word Juanito says a lot, especially when he is talking about his new *novia* (girlfriend) who is Mexican and sixteen, and flirts with other men.

For the first three days of class, William wore a giant Ross Perot Button on his shirt, hoping to encourage discussion about the presidential race, and what was wrong with their country to the north, but that was when the bemused glances started among the young people.

Although, it must be said: Teresa, another student in the class, is not exactly young. Teresa has a 17-year old son. William knows that from Teresa's family history, delivered in impeccably correct Spanish. William noted that she had failed to mention a husband. That's it! William suddenly thinks. He thinks he has discovered the source of his discomfort. None of the women in this class seem to be very interested in having a man!

Elena speaks little about her *esposo* (husband) back in Georgia. Mostly, she talks about Savannah and about art. Today, she takes from her woven bag a beautiful figure she has just completed in her sculpture class. The class oohs and gasps. It's a naked young girl in bronze, her carefree hair swaying sideways, and arms reaching up. After everyone admires it, *Que bueno! Que bonito!* (How wonderful! How pretty!) Elena says forlornly that tomorrow her husband is coming to spend a week.

"*Y vas al aeropuerto en León a recogerlo?*" Raul asks. Are you going to the airport in *León* to pick him up?

"Nooo," Elena says.

"*Por qué?*" Raul folds his arms. Why?

"*Sí, por qué no?*" William chimes in — Yeah, why not? — and before he knows it, Elena is passing one of those quick glances over to Maria, who is slipping into her seat, slightly out of breath. It was the kind of look his wife, his ex-wife that is, had given him when she said she didn't want to be married any more, a look that had said, you just don't get it, do you?

"*Porque*," Elena says, gripping the ankle of her statue. Because. *Porque* her time in the studio is valuable and it is much cheaper to bronze a work in Mexico than it is in the United States. She has to take advantage of the situation before she is forced to go back to Georgia and teach developmentally disabled fifth graders.

Elena sits back in her chair and looks grim.

Why don't you show up at the airport with a Spanish comb in your hair, he'll like it, William would have said, to offer a man's point of view, if the women had not been sending sympathy looks to Elena. He looks to Juanito for some manly support, but Juanito is holding his head up with one hand and doodling.

William had driven to San Miguel in his Toronado in a highly romantic state — leaving Los Angeles behind, free, just a man on the road. He'd expected to find love and nourish it with passionate gestures. He would meet a beautiful *señorita* and hire a *mariachi* band to serenade her under an open window after midnight, and she would hide inside, embarrassed and pleased. Instead, William had encountered a bewildering state of things — women doing art and other activities, escaping their men, seeming perfectly happy without them. William signed up for Spanish class, hoping it would be easier for him to talk to Mexican women, but he had to admit he didn't mind the prospect of meeting a lonely American either.

"*Buenas tardes, Maria*," Raul says when another class member slips in late. Good afternoon.

"*Te extrañábamos*," Juanito says. We missed you.

"*Mentiroso*," Maria accuses and everyone laughs. The words come too fast. William looks in his *diccionario. Mentiroso*. Liar. What would he do with a lively woman who hilariously calls men liars?

Maria is still laughing and nodding at what Raul is saying. She scribbles quickly in her notebook. Previously in class, she revealed she is a cook and photographer, living alone, exploring Mexican food for a cookbook. Thirty-five years old and never been *casada* — married. She never mentions a man either.

Raul at least understands him, William thinks.

"*Picarón?*" the teacher asks. William adjusts his bulk in the small wooden chair. "*Te emborrachaste el fin de semana pasad a cómo Juanito, Picarón?*" Did you get drunk this past weekend like Juanito?

Everyone laughs and William smiles. It pleases William to answer to *Pica-*

rón. Rascal. The first time he told a story in class, he talked about his boats, El Picarón and El Diablo. Raul never calls him Guillermo any more, only Picarón.

"Picarón," the teacher says, "*Que pasó?*" What's been happening?

William tried to think of a story that lives up to his name. "Last *noche,*" he begins.

"*Anoche,*" Raul says. Last night.

William adjusts his glasses. "*Anoche. Anoche, yo sabe.*"

"*Yo sabia?*" Raul wears a puzzled look. You knew?

"*Yo soy,*" William says. I am. "Yo soy drawing en *el jardín.*"

"*Yo dibujaba,*" Raul says. I was drawing.

"*Yo dibujaba,*" William mutters. But he's a can-do man; he squares his shoulders. "*Yo dibujaba porque* no tango enough *dinero* for *pintura.*" He didn't have money for paint because someone had warned him not to use the ATM machine at the Banamex on the *jardín,* that it gave smaller amounts than what customers asked for. William glides his fingernail under the word *pintura,* printed in large letters in his notebook, which he looked up before going to the art supply store with, as it turned out, not enough cash.

"*Sufficiente dinero para comprar pintura,*" Raul says. Enough money to buy paint.

William nods and rushes on. "*En los Estados Ulitos, yo* work with *pintura de* oil.*"

"*Los Estados Unidos,*" the teacher says, and rubs his forehead. "*Que es lo que quieres pintar, Picarón?*" What is it you want to paint?

"*Mis barcos,*" William says. My boats.

"*Claro. Que bueno.*" Of course. Great. Jesus grins. William relaxes.

"*Y que harás con tu obra?*" And what will you do with your paintings?

The answer is that William would like to paint a picture of his boats, sturdy figures on a rough and tumble sea, those great adventuring vessels, and give them to a sweetheart. William stares at the cross above the blackboard and tries to find the words. He wants to affect the casual, flippant tone that makes everyone in the class laugh. As he stares and thinks, the thought that he might never find a woman here in this beautiful Mexican town, or anywhere, surfaces and defeats him. He sighs and shrugs. "*Vender* — sell them," he says forlornly.

"*Bueno, Picarón! Quiere vender su obra. Picarón quiere ser rico,*" Raul says, teasing. Great, Picarón! He wants to sell his paintings. Picarón wants to be rich.

No. William thinks. I already am rich. That is not what I want.

From the neighborhood church comes the metallic clang of bells. The students rustle about, gathering books. William twists around to collect his Guatemalan pouch from the chair back and sees Elena's mouth open in an "O." He follows her gaze.

A tall man stands in the doorway, a travel bag behind him. His Panama hat is supposed to look rakish, William can tell, but topping the slightly alarmed expression on his face, it looks absurd. William knows how that feels and can hardly bear to look at the man. He looks instead at Elena who has crumpled in her seat, her hand still gripping the statue's leg. The class is oddly silent. William is suffocating; he has to get out, but the man stands frozen in the door. Nobody does anything. William shifts in his chair to make his move. Elena is still staring, but then William sees her hand move. He watches as the bronzed girl turns on her pedestal and reaches out for the man in the door. The chimes end their ancient song and a gong begins to toll — one, two, three — counting the beats of hope as they are forming in William's heart.

Susan McKinney de Ortega is a Philadelphia-born writer living in San Miguel de Allende since 1992. McKinney writes about raising a bicultural family with her Mexican husband in One Big Happy Family: 18 Writers Talk about Polyamory, Househusbandry, Mixed Marriage, Open Adoption and Other Realities of Truly Modern Love, *edited by Rebecca Walker (Riverhead Books, 2009). Selections from her unpublished memoir,* Flirting in Spanish *are included in* Mexico: A Love Story *(Seal Press, 2006);* Not What I Expected, The Unpredictable Road from Womanhood to Motherhood *(Paycock Press, 2007), sportliterate.com, 2009) and salonmagazine.com (1999). She has broadcast on National Public Radio, and has an essay forthcoming in the* Huffington Post. *Susan can pronounce many difficult words in Spanish but she has yet to master uncapping a Corona bottle with the seat belt latch, a task at which her Mexican husband is adept.*

San Miguel Brio

NICOLE BROUSSARD

ogs bark, roosters crow, and cries of *¡Elote!* echo through cobblestone *calles*. The squeal of truck brakes and the hi-lo tweets of a traffic whistle fill spaces in conversations. A motorcycle revs an unmuffled engine, straining up one of the steep hills. Pavlovian aromas — onions, peppers, and *chorizo* sizzling at taco stands — waft through the streets. Fuchsia bougainvillea, persimmon trumpet creeper, and yellow climbing jasmine escape over stone walls from hidden gardens, their flowering fingers reaching out to passersby. Fruit sellers, ice cream carts, seafood stands, and cafés beckon with tempting fare.

San Miguel has seen it all: love stories, the struggle for independence, religious pageantry and pagan ritual, bullfights and the famous Sanmigueladas, Mexico's running of the bulls. Time and again, San Miguel has grown beyond her borders, prosperity blessing her children with jobs and shoes and schools. She fills their bellies with the traditional *tortillas*, *frijoles*, and *carnitas*. She teases their senses with the pastels of high-desert cactus blossoms, the fragrance of tropical flowers, and a touch of the righteous fermentation of agave. Cool mountain winds travel valleys and arroyos spreading tendrils of magic into the city like love to a favored child. Nature conspires with her trickster energies to entice, inspire, and seduce.

As the sun eases over stone and adobe walls, cups of *café de olla* spice the senses. The early morning tranquility offers no clue to the rising tempo of the day. San Miguel is an outdoor girl except for late afternoons when shops, windows, and doors close to the heat. Then she retreats to the drowsy, indulgent *siesta*, to refresh herself for another evening of revelry.

Darkness rises, changing the heat from lethargy to hot-blooded energy racing through her streets. She holds court every night as the sun sinks behind high hills, thrilled by breast-pounding booms and light-flashing colors of firework displays filling the night skies. She smiles with indulgence at strolling mariachis singing ballads of love and betrayal. Old and young alike seek the music; it pours from doorways and spills down alleys, throbbing with passion.

The heart of the city and its people is the *jardín,* surrounded by deep-leafed laurel trees that shelter sidewalks and benches from the willful sun and late summer rains. It is the sparking ground of her magic.

She follows with interest two of her children: Laura, an old friend, and Michelle, a new arrival. She sighs with pleasure, rustling verdant leaves over the *jardín,* gathering her energies, as their stories unfold.

Michelle had celebrated her sixty-first birthday the previous night, alone, with take-out Chinese and a chilled bottle of *Pinot Grigio.* Birthdays were difficult. On her thirty-eighth birthday, a friend remarked, "You still look twenty-two. It's uncanny. How do you do it?" By her sixty-first birthday, explanations were impossible. Life in a new city seemed the perfect solution.

The attentive wind rode currents of exhilaration through the *jardín,* pulling ponytails, whipping newspapers and hats just out of reach, cooling the overheated brows of afternoon shoppers. Michelle tucked an unruly strand of hair behind her ear, unconscious of admiring glances cast her way. Resting on a bench, absorbed in the antics of a young Mexican family with two toddlers, she felt someone sit beside her.

"Hi, Michelle."

Michelle looked at the woman next to her in bewilderment, thrust into the memory of a childhood mystery: the disappearance of Laura Hanover.

Laura Hanover lived next door to Michelle and her family for ten years. She had filled a void in Michelle's life. Those were the fading days of aprons and house dresses. Mrs. Hanover, a pretty delicate-boned young woman with freckles scattered across her nose, wore both. Her favorite apron was white with red polka dots; the house dresses were dull nondescript colors worn with her one apparent idiosyncrasy, fringed brown-suede Indian moccasins.

She kept to herself, hiked the nearby fields and country lanes, read, cooked and tended her herb and vegetable gardens. Depending on the day's project, she radi-

ated subtle fragrances of vanilla, apples, or a vague sweetness reminiscent of cotton candy. On pasta days, the aromas of rosemary, basil, and oregano fresh from the earth, hovered like friendly clouds.

Michelle visited most afternoons after school. As she walked in the kitchen door, Mrs. Hanover would pat her arm or shoulder and hand her a cookie, gooey with warm chocolate chips or crumbling with nuts, dates, and brown sugar. Mrs. Hanover would ask about her day, but only if asked would she offer solutions to problems, solutions laced with wisdom and humor. She was an aberration in those days of the "better seen than heard" and "because I said so" attitudes of most adults.

The neighborhood women tolerated her as a throwback to another era. The neighborhood kids adored her. Each secretly wished Mrs. Hanover were her mother, instead of her own high-strung, bridge-playing, tennis-obsessed mother.

Mrs. Hanover's husband traveled. When seen, he was usually sprawled in the front yard in a frayed lawn chair, a six-pack of Budweiser at his feet, the grass high over his ankles, a can of beer raised in silent greeting to passing cars, accompanied by a good-natured grin.

The kids were the first to notice when Laura Hanover disappeared. Michelle's younger sister, Lisa, told their mom, "Mrs. Hanover isn't home and she wasn't there yesterday or the day before, either."

That evening the doorbell rang. Their father answered the door.

"Good evening, officers."

From the yellow halo of the porch light, baritone murmurs rolled into the foyer. The sisters peeked around the corner, holding their breath, still as statues, straining to hear the conversation.

"Marge, Jim Hanover called in from the road. He's concerned about his wife. Have you seen her this week?" their father called back into the house.

"I haven't spoken to Laura since last week. The children mentioned that she hasn't been home for days. I went over and called several times, but no one answered the door or the phone."

"We have a key to the house," Marge added.

Michelle's parents and the police went next door. The house was in perfect order. Mrs. Hanover's clothes filled the closet; aprons drooped on a hook in the pantry; one brown suede moccasin lay discarded by the kitchen door. The lingering scent of apple pie filled the still air.

And that was it. The disappearance of Laura Hanover: no clues, no follow-ups, nada.

Everyone except Michelle soon forgot her. At odd moments, throughout her life, Mrs. Hanover's face flashed through Michelle's mind accompanied by a whiff of warm cookies and Michelle would feel a haunting ache.

Laura Hanover patted Michelle's leg, bringing her back to the present. Laura's house dress and apron were long gone, replaced by a mid-calf skirt, long sweater, and fringed brown-suede boots. Silver bracelets jangled on her arm and blonde-streaked hair curled around her face. A roguish, expectant smile played on her lips.

"It's okay. You haven't lost your mind. It's me. I don't have any cookies for you, but maybe these will do." She handed Michelle a paper cone of warm, sweet *churros.*

Michelle automatically took the offering.

"Mrs. Hanover?"

Laura laughed, her head tilted in pleasure. "Call me Laura. It's so nice to see you. You were my favorite, you know. Tell me all about yourself."

"Mrs. Han...Laura, what's going on? You're here in Mexico and you're young. My mother's eighty-six. This isn't possible."

"Oh, honey, don't you remember? You must have been about nine years old when you told me you believed in magic," Laura said.

School was back in session, the air cool and crisp, anticipating winter. Mrs. Hanover's kitchen, with its red counter tops, yellow and white-flowered curtains, and harvest-gold refrigerator, was Michelle and her sister's second home. They sat at the white kitchen table in pools of sunlight. Lisa's short legs kicked her chair with dull thuds as she stuffed her mouth with cookies.

"So, girls, what exciting happened today?" Mrs. Hanover asked.

"A magician gave a show in the auditorium. He. . ."

Lisa cut Michelle off. "All the kindergarten kids got to sit on the floor right in front of the stage. He pulled a white rabbit out of his hat and he took a silver dollar out of my ear."

"It's not real magic, just tricks," Michelle said. "But I know there's real magic. I believe in it."

Cookie crumbs glittered on the corner of the table. Mrs. Hanover, absorbed in her thoughts, pressed the crumbs onto her finger, then licked them off.

"Magic is everywhere, but sometimes it's hard to hold on to." Mrs. Hanover *leaned forward, her sea-green eyes demanding Michelle's attention. "Everyone will tell you it can't be done, but I'll tell you the secret. Every time you bite into a chocolate-chip cookie, or tickle the tummy of a sun-warmed puppy, or gaze in awe at the beauty of a sunset, remember the joy. That's the real magic. Remember it and the magic will stay with you."*

She smiled at Michelle. "I have something extra for you today. A gift."

Mrs. Hanover hugged her with fierce concentration, whispering a musical incantation. Exhilarating warmth flowed through Michelle. When Mrs. Hanover released her, the return to reality startled Michelle, as an abrupt awakening in the middle of the night.

Then Laura Hanover patted their arms, kissed the tops of their heads, and sent them home with three cookies each wrapped in a white cloth napkin embroidered with bunches of red cherries.

"I think she's a fairy princess," Lisa said. She clasped her cookies to her chest as they crossed the Hanover's patchy brown-tipped grass back into their own dark green manicured yard. "I wish she had sung to me, too." She sighed, a sigh far too old for her five years.

Michelle remained silent.

"Many things are possible," Laura said, as they watched the Mexican family hoist sleepy toddlers onto their shoulders. "You've just forgotten. Come to my house for dinner tonight. I have a story to tell you that I should have told you years ago."

Michelle arrived at Laura's with a bottle of wine and an upset stomach. Hr hand shook as she knocked on the ancient wooden door that had a worn brass knocker shaped like a woman's hand. A Mexican houseman in blue pants and an embroidered shirt showed her in with old-world servility.

A three-tiered stone fountain trickled streams of sun-silvered water. Bright Talavera pots, overflowing with lacy-white baby's breath and trailing red, pink, and orange geraniums, encircled the fountain's base. Thick stone walls muted outside noises. The waning light blended the garden's brilliant colors into the muted canvas of a Monet painting.

Laura greeted Michelle with a hug, chuckling at her solemn expression.

"Don't worry. This is an extraordinary story, but you'll like it. I've only told it twice and neither time was I believed. It will only answer some of your questions though. I've had to learn appreciation for the not-knowingness of the world."

Laura led her into a dining room warmed by the patina of wealth and age to a dark Spanish table. A Mexican woman placed *molcajetes* of guacamole and salsa on the table and poured a Spanish *Rioja* into heavy green wine glasses. Laura held her glass up to the candlelight, her gaze turning inward as she focused on distant memories.

"I arrived in San Miguel in 1843, the summer of my twelfth birthday. It was a small town, a mix of Colonial mansions and *casitas de adobe* on dusty cobblestone streets that overlooked the Rio Obraje. That year was exceptionally dry; a fine powder of buff sand covered the roads and *mezquites*. After days of monotonous travel, our buckboard climbed the hill to Señor Rangel's house and we passed through the *jardín*, an open rock-paved area with a bubbling fountain. La Parroquia appeared like a welcoming promise, a pink castle in the late afternoon sun.

"José Rangel Ramirez, the trail master hired by my father, had led our wagon train from New York toward a never-reached destination. On the Santa Trail, late in the final leg of our journey, Señor Rangel left on a routine scouting mission. He returned to find the dead patiently waiting in the aftermath of the Indian massacre.

"A woman we had never seen before dragged two small boys and me under an overturned wagon. Maria, that was her name, held us in her arms with serenity, enclosing us in a bubble of golden light, a sanctuary of silence and safety. She entertained us with stories and games in the dry sand under the wagon while we awaited Señor Rangel's return.

"When Maria kissed us good-bye, she granted us each a wish. The boys asked for riches and heroic lives — the stuff of legends. I wished for a joyful life of magic and adventure forever, or at least for thousands of years, or for as many years as I wanted.

"Maria had laughed and said, 'Why not? But you must share it. You'll know when the time is right.'

"She slipped away as unobtrusively as she had arrived. Señor Rangel searched for hours before dismissing her as the fantasy of frightened children."

Candlelight from the silver candelabras cast shadows as wisps of music floated through the room. Michelle sipped her wine, spellbound by Laura's tale. She shivered as if in a cold breeze.

"Weary of the rugged trail, the heat and cold, the violence of white men, Indians, and banditos, Señor Rangel brought us home to Mexico and to his mother, *Doña* Julia. She loved and raised us as her own in the genteel protection of old-world Spanish tradition.

"I've always returned to this house. San Miguel de Allende is my home. I'm comfortable in this land where gold-leafed Virgins, draped in flowers and serenaded by church bells, are carried aloft in processional walks through the streets and where people still believe in everyday miracles.

"I've traveled the world and, on a few occasions, shared this mystifying gift. I have no answers other than this: I'm still young, healthy, and happy.

"I hope you'll forgive me for not telling you sooner." Laura relaxed in her seat and propped her feet on a neighboring chair. "That's my story — and yours."

Michelle pondered Laura's words as her anxiety dissolved. Michelle looked in wonder at her own hands, which were not the hands of a sixty-one year old woman.

"Are we young forever?" she asked.

"For as long as we want, I think. It's one of many unanswered questions. I haven't gotten to forever, yet."

Laura smiled, a wise smile that Michelle remembered from childhood, and leaned across the table to pat Michelle's arm.

Shafts of ivory moonlight careened through branches in search of darkness. The wind, heavy with scents of honeysuckle, slipped through the room, danced with candle-fire, then departed, leaving flower petals and perfume scattered in its wake. Gusts of air stirred leaves in the courtyard, breaking still shadows into animated fragments of dark and light, then glided out into the streets, following the music.

It was a good night for magic.

Nicole Broussard has lived in San Miguel de Allende for ten years. She divides her time between writing, gardening in the campo, hanging out with friends in town, and exploring the back-road wonders of Mexico with her partner, Steve.

There's a Hole in the Heavens

KATHLEEN KERSCH SIMANDL

Juanita stirred the bubbling *atole*, slowly. Each pop of the thick liquid seemed a hopeful release. The colorless morning light slitted around the edges of the curtain covering the front door in her aged mother's house in Ejido de Tirado. The neighbor's rooster crowed. Juanita had made the sweetened cornstarch drink extra thick this morning. When she let go of the spoon — which continued slogging around in circles — she reached to the splintery wooden shelf above the hotplate. This morning, she would add *canela*. Alejandra liked her *atole* with cinnamon and this was her oldest daughter's special day.

Juanita had made several decisions that morning. One was that she would let all five of her children, and her mother, sleep late. Muffled snores and puppy-like snorts came from the two bedrooms. She wanted a rare time alone to make a few more plans. Now, with the rich, spicy odor of the *atole* drifting to fill the entire three-room house, Juanita knew she didn't have much more time. Church bells tolling in the distance marshaled her thoughts: (1) Alejandra would get a job as a secretary in San Miguel...clang. (2) This would give her family enough pesos to buy a real roof for their house. . .clang, clang. (3) Her oldest son, Adolfo, would be able to pay *el pinche* Sanchez to get him into Texas. . .clang! clang! Clang! Each ring of the heavy bells lifted Juanita's hopes higher. "*Madre de Dios, socórranos en nuestra hora...*" the litany rolled, without conscious thought, from her mouth.

Suddenly, like a warning from the Blessed Mother herself, Juanita caught the coppery, chlorinated scent of rain in the air. Quickly switching her pan to the cool burner, she ran to get the sheets of plastic. Why today! Why, on

Alejandra's graduation day, should they have to deal with this? Drops splat-
ted, then clattered, on the patchwork of cardboard and tin panels spanning
the concrete block walls of their home. Juanita opened the first dusty sheet
of plastic with a pop and draped it over her bed.

At the sound, her mother opened her eyes. Then, with a start of realiza-
tion, the old woman wrenched herself out of bed and limped into the other
room to return with a second folded wad of plastic. She draped this over
her own narrow mattress, then, without pause, dragged the edge of the plastic sheet over her two cardboard boxes of clothing next to the bed. Juanita
dashed into the room where her *niños* were sleeping and did the same. All
five of the children were stirring now. Alejandra hurried to shelter her white
dress from the violation of the dirty drops puddling around the edges of the
plastic-covered bed.

Gracias a Dios, Juanita thought, that she didn't have to work on Sunday. She didn't mind cleaning house for the rich *gringos*, and, indeed, it was
through them that Alejandra had been given this chance. But this was a day
she wanted to devote to her family...and God. She hastily added the latter to
her thoughts, crossing her chest with practiced sweeps. She straightened the
heavy spoon which was almost submerged in the thickened *atole* and listened
to the now-pelting rain, and jabbering children's voices, with resignation.
The rooster crowed wetly, sounding dejected to have summoned such a gray,
muddy day.

Everything leading up to her bright daughter's graduation from the *prepa*
had been hard. The most difficult was having to deny the *niños* the few
pesos they always were begging for some *dulces* or a Coca-Cola. Also spirit-
crushing was having to beg the *señores* Amhurst for advances on her salary to
buy the books and uniform required by Alejandra's school. But she had done
it and her girl had done it. They both had done what was necessary. Juanita
had even made two *peregrinaciones* to the shrine in Atotonilco, many miles
on foot each way, to beg the Holy Virgin for her daughter's continued success in preparing for a secretarial job. Juanita lowered her eyes as she poured
the steaming *atole* into their four chipped cups, feeling a little smile of pride
turning up the corners of her lips. She again crossed her chest with pious
afterthought.

Now dressed in white, and looking beautifully virginal, Alejandra joined
her mother in front of the hotplate. Tilting her chin up, she pulled the string

to turn on the single light bulb wired above the kitchen part of the house. It flickered and popped once in the damp, but it held, brightening the gloom within the suffocating little house. Alejandra smiled.

"Mama! This is it! This is the day I stop taking from you. I am no longer a little girl."

"Ah, but you are still my little *nena*. Perhaps there have been some sacrifices, but that is a price I have willingly paid. God smiles on the pride I have in you!"

Mama! Everything will be good now...no more hard times. Just wait and see."

Tears of joy threatened to spill from Juanita's eyes, like water seeping up from the *artesian* well near Atotonilco.

Alejandra, misinterpreting the font of the emotion, hastened to add, "Don't worry, Mamacita! Last night, Julio told me he wanted to marry me. He says so many pretty things. And, Mama, he's going to get a real good job in construction. He even says maybe he'll let me work as a secretary later."

A drop of rain hit the burner of the hotplate and sizzled into silence.

Kathleen Kersch Simandl is a veteran of almost 20 years of teaching art & English in the public schools of Wisconsin. Having survived that, she decided to take the plunge into a very different existence: retiring and living, full-time, in Mexico. And, although most of her earlier writing efforts consisted of non-fiction articles in teaching/trade magazines and newspapers, she has now become more involved in both photography and in writing fiction — particularly "flash fiction" for on-line literary publications. Kathleen has won several minor awards for writing and photography. And, most recently, she has had a story included in a Chicken Soup for the Soul *anthology.*

The Twelve Steps for Learning Spanish in San Miguel de Allende

KIMBERLY KINSER

1. I am powerless over the Spanish language and my life has become unmanageable. Life could be manageable if I chose to speak only English, which is possible in this community rich in *gringos* and English-speaking Sanmiguelenses.

2. Came to believe that one of the many Spanish schools could restore me to sanity.

3. Made a decision to turn my will and my life over to the six power verbs: *yo puedo, yo quiero, yo necesito, yo tengo que, me gusta, yo voy.*

4. Made a fearless and searching moral inventory before giving up and dropping out convinced that the Spanish language was beyond my reach.

5. Shared with *mi maestro, mis amigos, y mi esposo* the exact nature of my decision to be satisfied to order food in Spanish only and use English in other situations.

6. Asked God to remove these shortcomings. Time to involve God. Nothing else has worked.

7. Humbly returned to class.

8. Made a list of all the reasons that I wanted to learn Spanish and move to San Miguel in the first place.

9. Went to class every day that class was scheduled. Did my homework whenever possible.

10. Continued to attend class and do homework and to speak Spanish every-day.

11. Sought through volunteerism and any other method necessary to improve my contact with Spanish speaking persons finally understanding that learning a language is a process that cannot be rushed or pushed but only experienced and explored.

12. Practice Spanish in all of my affairs, including the telephone and be an example to other non-Spanish speakers that it is possible, through the use of these steps to learn a foreign language and integrate into a foreign culture.

Kimberly Kinser has lived winters in San Miguel since 2004. She leads creative writing workshops in San Miguel using the Amherst Writers and Artist method. She has written for Atención, *English language newspaper in San Miguel, and was a contributor to the first* Solamente en San Miguel. *Each summer she returns to Coyle, Washington.*

My Vanity

MANJA ARGUE

She sits on Umaran
Just down from the Parroquia
In a doorway
On a concrete step.

Her fingers twisted,
wrapped into a ball,
like the crochet yarn
I use with such ease.

I drop my coin
into her basket, she smiles
"Gracias Señora,"
her head bobbing,
she glances up at me.

I wonder what meager
supplies can be bought
with so little,
tortillas, perhaps some fruit
or rice, beans.

As for me,
I wondered…have I bought a lost

layer of my soul that I
discarded so long ago?

I walk away
admire my hands
my long slender fingers
I've always liked my hands.
My vanity.

Manja Argue lived in San Miguel de Allende from 2002 to 2009 where she has pursued the art of poetry and short story writing. Most recently she has been writing Flash Fiction, which is a short story of from 300 to 1000 words. She has self-published three bilingual chap books, The Wolf Approaches/El Lobo Se, The Slide/El Tobogán, Passing/Transito *and one book in English only,* Short Stuff. *Currently she resides in Oakland, California where she is still writing poetry and stories.*

The Three Kings

CYNTHIA HUNTINGTON

I t was a cold, dark, starry evening as I walked down Ancha de San Antonio, on my way to a house party celebrating The Three Kings. This was to be an adult version of the children's party, held on January 6th, when Mexican children receive presents. I was new to Mexico and to this charming town so I looked forward to a night out, experiencing an unfamiliar celebration and meeting new friends.

Since arriving in San Miguel, my days and nights had been busy remodeling my bed and breakfast in a centuries-old home. As a result, I had not met many of the interesting-looking people I saw walking by every day. I was excited about meeting new friends, yet my former husband's parting words rang in my ears as our thirty-year marriage ended in divorce.

"No man of my age looks at a woman of your age. I am the last man in your life. Just live with me, Sheila, at least it will cover your medical insurance." I didn't reply.

At that point, I had not thought of Mexico, but after taking a painting course in Guadalajara, I visited San Miguel. This, I decided, is where the past could become the past. My children were emancipated with busy lives of their own. There was little to keep me in the cold Northeast.

I met Emily, our hostess, on one of the weekly House and Garden tours. She sat next to me on the bus and we immediately became friends. Our chat during the tour and late lunch revealed we had been living parallel lives. We both grew up outside North America, she from Chile and I from the North of England. Both of us attended Drew University in New Jersey, then lived in the United States for many years. Now we lived only two blocks apart.

Several weeks later, she invited me to this party, promising a good mixture of interesting men and women.

When I arrived at the party, the house was chilly so I was glad to have worn my most attractive woolen sweater and long skirt. We took turns warming ourselves near the fire that gave off a woodsy aroma. There was a good mixture of Canadians, US Americans and Mexicans and conversations were in both English and Spanish. Most guests appeared to be single or engaged; few wedding rings were visible.

Emily took my hand and introduced me to each guest by name — not that I would remember many of the names. The exceptions were several fun women and a good looking well-dressed Mexican man in his early sixties whose name was Max. While guests mingled and the conversations were lively, I noticed Max looking at me whenever I glanced his way. I felt a mixture of embarrassment and excitement. I decided to keep my back or my best side toward him to avoid eye contact.

Before midnight rang its twelve bells, Emily carried out a large wooden cutting board with a huge circular, sugar-coated yeast-bread sprinkled with small pieces of green and red angelica. She instructed each of us to cut a slice and, if we found a small white plastic baby in our piece, we were obliged to give another party within the month. What fun, I thought, but I hoped not to find one in my piece. My house wasn't ready for a party yet.

To my relief, there was no baby in my piece and so my attention turned to see who would get the doll. We all watched carefully, making sure no one tried to swallow it, hide it in their cheek or in their serviette to avoid hosting a party. The crowd became quiet as each newly-cut piece was eaten. Max joyfully presented the doll. He collected names and phone numbers and promised to invite us all to his party. Mine was the first name and number he took.

The clock chimed one. I thanked Emily for the delightful evening and collected my wrap. Emily said, "Please call me as soon as you get home." As I left, Max caught up with me and said, "I'd be happy to drive you home — if I may." I replied, "No thank you, Max. I live nearby and I'd rather walk on this lovely evening."

"Oh, well, here's my card." he said. "I'd like to have coffee and chat with you sometime in the very near future. Please give me a call." He spoke clear English without hesitation.

We walked out together. As he got in his car I called out, "I'll call you tomorrow." He smiled and I watched his car disappear up the cobbled street. I turned to walk in the opposite direction, when something caught my eye across the dark street. A small metallic object twinkled about three feet above ground. It was almost hidden under the boughs of the trees; its reflection flitted between the low branches. Curious, I crossed the street to find it was the reflection from a horse's bridle. To my relief, I saw two mounted policemen. As I walked towards them, I noted the quality of their Arabian horses, and, on a whim, I said boldly, in my poor Spanish, "*Buenas noches, Señores Yo quero su caballo, por favor.*" "Good evening gentlemen. I want your horse, please."

To my astonishment, one policeman quickly dismounted. He handed me the reins and stood back to let me mount. I hitched up my long skirt, fitted my 5th Avenue boot into the stirrup and swung my other leg over the saddle. We trotted merrily down the street, one policeman trotting along my right and the other running on foot, on my left. As we turned the corner on to Ancha de San Antonio, a taxi passed by and the driver leaned out and asked jokingly, "*¿Hey, que pasa?*" "What's up?" And my happy reply was "*Feliz año Nuevo.*" "Happy New Year."

The runner on my left smiled, but he was panting heavily. I could tell just what he looked like when he was a baby; that sweet angelic face looking up at this crazy *gringa* riding his horse in the middle of the night. But he must have been crazy too, to allow this.

When we arrived at my door, I swung my leg over and slid off the saddle onto the cobbles below and with, "*Muchos gracias, muy amable.*" and a few blown kisses in their direction, I entered my colonial casa. When the door was closed, I heard their horses' hooves on the cobbles as they left.

I hurried through the courtyard, entered the kitchen and telephoned Emily, to say, "I'm home", who replied somewhat bewildered, "How did you get home so fast?" I answered, "On all fours. I rode home on a policeman's horse." Emily shrieked with delight, and said "Only in Mexico."

Cynthia B Huntington worked as an au-pair in Copenhagen and went to cooking school in the evenings. She also worked in Lyon France. After working as a registered nurse from Yorkshire, England, she became a Pan American Airline stewardess. In the early 1960's, she married a Turkish professor, and lived in

Istanbul with her in-laws. Huntington has worked for 30 years in the States and relocated to San Miguel Allende Mexico, where she is writing memoirs and short stories.

Accident

Sarah Aptilon

or the past ten months, the first ten months of our son Leonardo's life, I have written down the things he does so I will remember them later:

The way his hands open like flowers when he nurses.

The way he laughs in his sleep.

The way he desperately wants whatever I have in my hands, cries bitterly and then forgets.

And today, on the road to San Miguel de Allende from Mexico City, in the parking lot of a truck stop restaurant, the way he holds his face to the wind, breathing in the air that sweeps across the plains, fragrant with the smell of warm grasses. The late-afternoon sunlight shines on the fields and big trucks idle nearby. I wish I could put him down to crawl on the little patch of grass under the trees by the parking lot. In our neighborhood in Mexico City there is no real grass where he can crawl.

I change him, nurse him, and then he is climbing all over the car. He stands on his father's lap and grabs the steering wheel, holds himself up, leans forward like he's driving. I watch him sideways, in a strange veiled light. I want to keep him in my sights and not let him go. Not after what we have just seen on the road to San Miguel.

We don't really have time to go away this weekend. Leonardo is teething and hasn't been sleeping through the night, and Alex and I have been too busy worrying about things like whose credit card we are going to get a cash advance from so we can pay the electricity before they shut it off.

But we go anyway. My writing teacher Janice, whom I've never met in person, is in San Miguel and I want to visit her before she goes back to New York. This road, writing, opens before me too, windswept, unfurling with promise. I am finally writing and she appears along the way as if by chance but, I believe, probably not.

In the hotel room I wake to see Leonardo standing in his crib, smiling at me. He clamps his mouth onto the bar of the crib's frame and then utters little cries, ma-ma-ma-ma-ma, waiting for me to come and get him. Outside it's still dark but church bells chime in the distance, signaling the start of the day.

Since he was born I have learned that life is out of my hands. That our three hearts keep beating, moment after moment—that is beyond my control. It is a feeling of peace.

We have breakfast in the courtyard of our hotel, the Posada de la Aldea, which looks like an old monastery even though it was built in 1979. After breakfast we walk to the *jardín*, the main square, and sit on a bench in front of the Parroquia, the town's baroque and neo-Gothic cathedral. Leonardo naps in the pouch on Alex's chest, almost too big for it now, his long legs dangling, soothed in his sleep by the sounds of the people all around him, the three different mariachi bands playing in separate corners of the square, the couples talking, the squeak of the balloon man's whistle. A balloon dachshund with wheels bobs behind the balloon man on a string leash. The cathedral floats ahead of us, pink and Disneyesque. Two palm trees shake like pompoms on either side of the church, swaying in the wind, their fronds glittering in the sunlight.

It looks like some fantastical combination of the bell towers of Notre Dame and the spires of the cathedral of Milan, says Alex, an architect.

I read that the architect drew the plans for this church in the dirt with a stick, I say.

According to the myth, he did.

I watch the palm trees sway and sparkle in the sun, and I remember how when Leonardo was born, after the caesarian, the nurse held his cheek against my cheek, so warm and soft, and he looked into my eyes and then she took him away too soon. Alex carried him to the nursery and they wheeled me to the recovery room and I lay there impatient, anxious, full of love, and through the tinted hospital window I watched three big trees in the distance tossing in the wind, jubilant, waving their branches to me in blessing.

I go to buy ice cream from the cart on the corner of the square, and a little boy with a dirty face and runny nose asks me for a coin. Maybe when you get your change, he says, looking up at me with a hopeful expression. Of course they are here too, like the children in Mexico City who roam the streets late at night, who sell Chiclets and stand on their hands at traffic lights and paint their faces like clowns and tap on the windshields of cars and stop to ask the people eating in cafés for a peso, always looking down, with an indifferent sorrowful shrug. He is too young for this. Where are his parents? The man next to me buys him an ice cream and I give him all my change but it is not enough.

Once we get past the choke of traffic surging out of the city, the road from Mexico City to San Miguel is a beautiful drive that passes through sweeping high Velasco plains and skies, scrub brush and rugged trees, mountains moving like waves in the distance, the land not flat but undulating, rising and falling. Clusters of cactus decorate the hillsides, and maguey stalks rise like columns of smoke against the sky.

Just before the truck stop, before the turnoff to San Miguel, as the road curves left a police officer stands in the right lane, directing traffic away from the side of the road, an ominous gesture. We come around the corner and a scene of desolate stillness flashes into view and then is gone.

I look, because I look at everything. An ambulance sits idle, its lights flashing. A ruined SUV is there, its front windows a tangle of twisted gaping metal. I don't see any other cars. Things are scattered nearby—blankets, duffel bags, a sleeping bag. A human shape lies on the ground among the bags, covered with a quilt. And another, closer to the road. A police officer stands waiting for something. A curious peace hovers over the scene, the crisis passed.

All this appears in the beautiful late-afternoon light, the soft air of early evening. As we drive on I notice fluffy little weeds growing wild along the median, their spiked fronds lit up, catching the light, softly tossing in the wind.

Don't look. Why did you have to look? Alex says.

They drive like maniacs on these roads, he says. Or else they're drunk.

I blame the government, he says. There are no speed limits, no driver's tests.

I am doing the same thing in my mind, turning it first one way and then another. I imagine the two people still hovering nearby, watching in disbelief from above. In one moment, at this curve in the road, they have departed from this world, leaving their bundles and blankets behind.

A Buddhist teacher once told me that when we see that something terrible has happened we should ask forgiveness, because on some deep level we are part of it and it is part of us.

And yet as we drive on, and then when we park at the truck stop and I feel the chilly wind on my face, the shadows lengthening around us, and the nausea of death is still with me, I also feel more alive, filled with the dumb gratitude of one who has been spared.

Without knowing it we have chosen a hotel that is almost next door to Janice's house. At noon we walk down the quiet cobblestone street. No one is around. Her house is near the end of the road, a vertical two-story structure painted a deep Mexican turquoise blue, with a big cross on the outside.

We bought this house from missionaries, she says. When we first moved in people still called asking about mass.

She wears a tailored brown dress and black leggings, and pink glasses studded with rhinestones at the edges. Her voice is welcoming, musical. Until now we have talked only by phone and email. She has edited one of my stories, shined a light on it, rendering visible what I could not see before.

She takes us on a tour of the house, all the way up to the rooftop terrace with a view of the mountains and the city with its frilly pink church. On the lower terrace a pair of budgies, one blue and one yellow, twitter and hop in a cage. In the living room hangs a painting of her daughter flying across an imagined sky, a magical bird with the face of a girl.

We sit and talk under a big umbrella on the terrace as the afternoon sunlight rings down around us like music, a single bright insistent note. Leonardo sleeps on the sky-blue rug in the living room, sheltered from the heat of the day.

We never planned to have children, Janice says. But then after years of this bohemian life we changed our minds. We adopted our daughter from Guatemala.

She says this as though it still surprises her but you do what you have to do, no arguments.

After that, when *Ms.* magazine called her about an article on women who choose not to have children, she had to say she was no longer comfortable talking about that subject.

Leonardo stirs and I watch him through the screen door. He sits up and looks around, then pulls himself up holding onto the arm of the couch.

All he wants is to be vertical, I say.

It's like the urge to make art, Janice says.

She has a lot of courage, Alex says later, as we walk back up the road toward our hotel. The intellect is one thing, the heart is another.

Along the way we meet a shy old man standing with two burros laden with herbs from the sierra. The burros regard us with knowing glances and Leonardo turns to look at them, but then he goes back to trying to grab Alex's sunglasses off his face and the burros go back to pulling up grass beside the sunlit road.

The next morning on our way out of town we stop at the lookout point at the top of the hill. We find our hotel in the distance, a tiny toy model with its miniature courtyard and puffs of trees. From here we can see how the town is set in the curve of the land, the plain sweeping up into the surrounding mountains, and I feel the deep good of the place, blown away by the wind, fainter now, diaphanous, already out of reach.

Sarah Aptilon is a writer and translator who lives in Mexico City with her husband Alejandro Aptilon and their son, Leonardo. She holds a B.A. in East Asian Studies from Yale University and a Ph.D. in Religious Studies from Stanford University. During her undergraduate studies she took a hiatus to spend seven years in a Buddhist monastery in Kyoto. She is currently at work on a collection of short stories set in Japan.

Música en Vivo
(Chicago, Illinois)

SARAH RAE

Multi-colored pictures of painted food float on green and blue walls.

Tacos con arroz y frijoles. Burritos. Mojarra. Carnitas. Carne Encebollado. Tortas. Pollo asado.

Waitresses in long red jackets, short red miniskirts, and knee-high black boots serve the men beer. Their white blouses have low necklines and frilled ruffles.

The men wear faded jeans and work shirts. They sit and stare with red-rimmed eyes. They gaze at the women who serve them, at the band, into their beers, vacantly ahead.

Outside, a siren wails.

TV monitors show videos of large-figured ladies who wear less than the waitresses. They talk on the screen to fully dressed, heavy-set men in tight, ill-fitting suits.

The wind howls.

The band plays *cumbias*. The base line thumps, dominates. Like a funeral dirge.

The women take orders from the men. They sit with them and talk to them, drink with them and make them laugh. Dance with them. Sway back and forth with them.

In between songs, the lead guitarist names Mexican states.

Zacatecas. Guanajuato. Jalisco. San Luis Potosi. Morelos. Chihauhua. Durango. Michoacán.

The men cheer for their homelands. They order more beer.

Waitresses bring translucent plastic pitchers with fake frost etched in.

Corona. Sol. Dos XX. Negro Modelo. San Miguel.

The el train roars by.

In the women's bathroom, a waitress weeps. El Delgado en la Mesa 10 has just told her he's going back.

Freezing rain drops.

He's already bought his ticket. The bus leaves from 26th Street. It departs the next afternoon. He'll be home by Christmas.

Applause comes from the TV monitors. The band takes a break.

Two waitresses sit down at Table 14. Table 12 orders more Modelo.

Ice starts to crust the sidewalks. The trees. The snow.

Red and green neon signs flash in the window. They say: *Baile esta noche.*

Sarah Rae teaches high school English. She has been fortunate to have the opportunity to study in San Miguel de Allende with the University of New Orleans, from which she is pursuing an MFA in creative writing. She has previously been published in the Tata Nacho Press and in the Poet's Corner of the online arts journal fieralingue. *She lives in Chicago with her beautiful and spunky gray cat, Maya.*

Blond Bullfighter

Eva Hunter

otty Vidargas came to San Miguel de Allende in 1947 as one of over 100 World War II veterans who used their G.I. Bill benefits to study art at the Academia de Belles Artes, a former convent turned art school. Dotty has become a town legend. She was a picadora in central Mexican bullfights for a time, married a local Mexican man, and raised four children while she pursued a series of careers as varied as interior decorator, creamery owner and manager, and finally the town's first realtor. In the story that follows, Vidargas tells how she came to be involved in the corrida de toros *as surely Mexico's only* picadora.

"My first thought was 'God, do I have to ride this thing?' I was not in the least impressed with my mount. I'll be honest: When I had agreed to be a *picadora* the night before in the bar, I'd imagined myself riding a dashing steed. But this horse was a poor old thing, with padding on his right side, and a blindfold over one eye. And anyway, I was no longer as sure in the light of day that this was such a good idea. Last night, after a few drinks, I had wanted to do it. But what if I made a complete fool of myself?

"The night before, I was probably the only woman in La Cucaracha, a bar in the small Central Mexican town of San Miguel de Allende. Proper Mexican women were never found in bars like La Cucaracha, with its dark wooden screens set just inside the doors—a barrier that spared women and children the indignity of seeing the drinkers inside.

"But I was not yet a Mexican wife attached to a traditional Mexican family. I was a *gringa*, a Norteamericana, and I was blonde, and petite, and pretty, and 24 years old. It was 1947, and I'd been here less than a year, study-ing art on the G.I. Bill, in a former convent a couple of blocks away on

Hernandez Macias street. There were perhaps 150 other young Americans, all in their 20s and 30s, studying at the art school—and all, like me, World War II veterans. We had spent our early adult years serving our country, and undergoing rationing; some of us giving up our studies at colleges or universities. We'd done it without regret—we were part of the war effort. After the war, I'd studied art in Chicago for a year, then—through a friend's influence—decided to use my G.I. Bill money to go to school in this place in the middle of Mexico I'd never heard of. It would be an adventure, and something different. I promised my mother, who had remained in Chicago after my father's death, that I wouldn't stay longer than six months, although I secretly doubted I would keep that promise.

"I was a little rowdy in those early days, even compared to the other *gringos,* and I was gregarious. We, the North Americans here on the G.I. Bill, formed the town's first interaction with "Americans," and with the short-sightedness of youth, I had little concern for how my antics must have appeared to them.

"The Cucaracha was one of several bars where my friends and I gathered. At first I interacted with the other students from art school: American men and a few other former-G.I. women. But we all got to know the Mexican men from good families who frequented the bar. There was a nicer place, the Posada de San Francisco, where proper Mexican women might be seen—but at La Cucaracha the liquor was cheap. The establishment was casual, at times verging on grimy. But I liked the atmosphere of the two rooms. The smaller room in back was the bar, and the front room was filled with the typically uncomfortable Mexican straight-backed wooden couches, softened only by a few faded and worn pillows.

"On that particular day, I'd spent five or six hours in my studio on the second floor of the Belles Artes. I shared it with a couple of other students, and frequently we set up our easels on the terrace overlooking the crumbling, but beautiful interior of the former convent. I returned to the house I shared with some other students in the late afternoon, but around nine or ten that night, I decided to go back down the hill to *centro*. I knew it would probably be lively in town, as the next day was the beginning of a festival which would include fireworks, music, and a bullfight—a *corrida de toros*.

"San Miguel de Allende is a town built on hills. We lived on the Salida de Querétaro, which would probably best translate to "the road to Querétaro." The *salida* was one of the main roads out of town, and from our house on the hill we could see the entire city with its picturesque seventeenth century buildings and colorful streets.

"To get to the center of San Miguel, I walked down the hill a ways, then made a left turn onto Correo street. This street was a straight shot to the *jardín,* but it was steep, and sometimes the cobblestones were broken or missing. It led between high walls that were painted in shades of reds, terra cottas, greens, yellows, and blues. These continuous outer walls joined individual houses that were often centuries old. Four blocks of varying length got me into the town's center—with the *jardín* on the right, and the high spires of the pink-toned Parroquia on the left.

"I cut diagonally through the *jardín,* whose paths were bordered with laurel trees trimmed into boxy shapes. A lacy wrought-iron kiosk with a blue-green dome was in the middle of this town square, and paving stone paths surrounded by red and purple flowering bushes led up to it. Diagonally through the *jardín,* about 20 broad steps led down to the street. La Cucaracha was under the *portales:* covered arches that sheltered the sidewalks on the *jardín's* east and west sides.

"The bar was hopping, and I had a drink or two with a couple of my friends. Maybe the invitation was meant as a joke, I don't know. But two men whom I had known on a casual basis came up to me after I'd been there for awhile. One of them—I can't remember either of their names now—said to me, 'We've heard you like horses.'

"I was an expert horsewoman. I'd ridden since I was three, and I didn't stop riding when I came to San Miguel. Word had gotten around.

"Yes," I answered. "I do like horses." Why were they asking this, I wondered. I invited them to sit down.

"It seems they were connected to the production of the *corrida de toros* that would take place the next day, because they asked me if I would like to ride as a *picadora.*

"A *picadora?* I looked at my friends, but they weren't any help.

"'What's a *picadora?'* I asked.

"And so it was explained. A *picador* is the person who thrusts a spear, called a *garrocha,* into the muscle at the back of the bull's neck. The loosening of the muscle forces the bull to drop his head, allowing the *torero* to work the bull with his cape.

"I was a little surprised at this invitation. And I was hesitant to say yes, because I didn't know what I would be getting into. 'That sounds interesting, ' I said. But, still, I wasn't sure. I had never heard of any women who played the *picador* role. But after a little time, and a few more drinks, I agreed. A bullfight was very Mexican, and by then I was in love with Mexico. I wanted to be part of all things Mexican.

"The plan was that I would be picked up from my house the next morning for a fitting in some borrowed *traje corto:* a flat-brimmed black sombrero, a short black jacket, and long black pants worn with short boots.

"I awakened the next morning excited and a little fearful. What had I gotten myself into? But the men arrived as scheduled, and I was taken to the house of a friend of theirs—a woman from an old San Miguel family. She loaned me her *traje corto.*

"By shortly after three that afternoon, I was in the *plaza de toros* waiting just outside the ring with the horses and the rest of the team. I would be one of two *picadors* who worked with the bullfighter we had been assigned to.

"The *plaza de toros* in San Miguel is in the center of town: four blocks from the *jardín* and Parroquia, two blocks up Correo street past the post office, then a right turn on Recreo, down a block and one-half past the elementary school, to the red-painted double doors that were each large enough to let a truck pass through.

"The ring itself was a typical old colonial bull ring—not huge, like the ring in Mexico City, but relatively small and intimate. The seats were on tiers of cement, softened only by cushions that people brought in or rented for the afternoon.

"The more expensive tickets read '*la sombra.*' They were in the shade. The cheap seats were across the ring, in the sun. Vendors wandered the stands, selling peanuts and beer, candy and tequila.

"Here's how a bullfight is organized. It's divided into thirds, called *suertes,* and each third is announced by a trumpet call. At the beginning, the participants parade into the ring to salute the presiding dignitary, accompanied by a *pasadoble*: the driving, almost militaristic music associated with bullfights.

"The bull then enters the ring, and the *peones*—members of the bullfighter's team—take him through various simple passes before the *matador* works him with his magenta and gold cape. This is done so the *matador* can observe the bull's behavior.

"Next, the *picador* enters on horseback. *Picadors* are not the most popular of people. When the *picador* punctures the bull just behind the mound of muscle on the bull's neck, this is the first loss of blood. If the crowd feels the *picador* has done too much to weaken the bull, they boo. The *matador* continues to observe closely, because the manner in which the bull charges the horse gives the *matador* clues about the bull's temperament and how he will perform when he is worked with the *muleta,* or smaller cape.

"After this, the *banderilleros* plant colored barbs, *banderillos,* in the bull's neck . This is meant to anger the bull, as well as to invigorate him.

"The final stage is called 'the third of death.' Here the *matador* enters the ring with a small red cape, and a sword. The *matador* uses this cape to lead the bull through a series of beautiful ritual passes to help his head go lower. Eventually he maneuvers the bull into the correct position where he is then able to stab him between the shoulder blades. If the kill has been skillful, the bull drops immediately. If the *matador* has performed well, the crowd may wave white handkerchiefs to petition the official to award the bullfighter an ear, or even two.

"Of course, I did not know all of this at the time, and neither was I thinking about the art or sport of what was about to happen. It's true that I had done some unusual things in my life. When, just before college, I was sent to a 'guest ranch' in Colorado to have a pampered riding vacation, another guest—a cute guy—and I worked as horse wranglers instead.

" I was one of the first female air traffic controllers as a WAC during World War II, but I had requested duty as a pilot. No dice on that one, though, because women weren't being trained to be fighter pilots!

"But I'd never before done anything quite this daring. A *picadora?* I was concerned about whether or not the crowd would accept me, and about whether I would get it right. And, frankly, whether or not I was about to humiliate myself.

"The other *peones* explained what I was to do. On my horse, I was to turn right as soon as I entered the ring, then about a quarter of the way around, I was to turn the horse inward and wait until the *matador* caped the bull to my horse. They explicitly, emphatically, told me not to ride to the center of the ring for the bull. The bull is supposed to come to you, they cautioned.

"I was handed the long solid-wood *garrocha,* which ended with a steel point. I was surprised that it was so heavy. This made me even more nervous. It was time to go in for the third *suerte.* The other *picador* and I went in. I rode to the right, as instructed. But the *matador* couldn't seem to get the bull near me. Minutes passed, and I thought, now what? Still, the *matador* was unable to maneuver the bull in my direction. I waited a little longer, then finally thought: This is silly. I have to do something.

"I took my horse a few steps toward the middle of the ring. The bull didn't come. Another few steps. He didn't come. Further into the ring, thinking, O.K., surely the bull will come my direction now.

"Suddenly, he charged! He hit the side of my horse with an impact that practically threw me from the saddle. But I stood up in the stirrups and *pic'*ed him in exactly the right place, leaning hard on the *garrocha.* And surprised myself by doing it right!

"My adrenalin was charging. The public was making a lot of noise, but I couldn't tell whether they were booing or cheering. Sweat streamed down my face. The trumpet blew. I left the ring.

"All I could think was: At least I didn't make a fool of myself. The guys said, 'Why did you go in the middle of the ring? We told you not to.'

"From then on I was a sensation. I was given a good horse to ride in the *corridas,* and was featured on bullfight posters all over Central Mexico, along with the *matadors.*

"A month or so after my bullfighting career began, I sat outside at Los Dragones, a café near the jardín, drinking coffee and reading a copy of *The Chicago Tribune.* As I browsed the society pages, making comments about this notice or that to a friend, I saw a photograph of a blonde in a flat-brimmed Mexican sombrero. 'I think I know that face,' I said.

"Suddenly I started, and nearly dropped the newspaper. The photograph was of me! 'Against Mother's Orders' the headline read.

"I sat, stunned, staring at the newspaper. It was a syndicated news service story about my unusual role in Mexico as a *picadora.* How on earth had they found out?

"And what was I going to tell my mother?"

Eva Hunter is an award-winning writer who has published professionally for over 20 years. Her area of specialization is short and long literary nonfiction, but she also writes literary fiction. She has taught creative writing as faculty at Portland State University, at the Art Museum School of Portland, and privately in both the United States and Mexico. A popular writing conference speaker, she is co-founder of the Portland, Oregon based Connexus, The Writer's School, and The Writer's Workshop: San Miguel in Mexico. Eva's writing credentials include The New York Times Magazine, Quii, The Quarterly, Northwest Magazine, Oregon Magazine, Portland State Magazine, The Oregonian, Oregon Business Magazine, the Boston Herald *and many others. Eva teaches courses in fiction as well as nonfiction through the Writer's Workshop: San Miguel. She is currently writing a memoir about growing up near Las Vegas in the 60s:* A Little Mormon Girl.

Learning To Walk on Cobblestones: The Mexican Way

ROLAND SALAZAR ROSE

My father never expressed what he felt about San Miguel's cobblestones. My wife and I would lead him by the hand to the center of town, a short walk for a regular walker, about ten minutes down a steep hill. Going up was something else, especially with Reggie in tow. We had to take a taxi. Taxis in San Miguel are ubiquitous and reasonable; they only cost about one U.S. dollar back when my father was living here. Like my grandfather, my father was always a fast walker. From our home in Los Balcones, he would set off with the same sense of purpose as when he would alight from the 8th Avenue Subway at Lexington Avenue on his way to work. In San Miguel, he walked too quickly, without looking carefully, and it's impossible to walk that way unless you were born and raised here. I often wonder how the native people here, both young and old, seem to float over the adjourns, or paving stones. Like apparitions they move, seldom, if ever, tripping, while the rest of us gringos pick out each footfall, as if climbing the face of Mount Washington. When Reggie lived here, nearly all the streets cobblestones, and the sidewalks were made of marble, which was supplied many years ago from a now-defunct quarry. These stones are often removed and replaced by laborers hundreds of times for street and sidewalk repairs. Driving around town, you inevitably run into streets that are undergoing repairs — usually because of broken water mains or to lay wires for telephone, electricity, and cable television. The wires are buried in order to preserve the colonial style of San Miguel's central area, which was named a United Nations World Heritage Site in 2008.

Sitting in the jardín, the main square, looking at the Parroquia, the unusual church with its façade of pink limestone, I admire its neo-gothic, multi-towered façade that has been disparagingly called "grotesque" by architectural purists. I think not! And so do many tourists to San Miguel. It faces the jardín and is photographed and painted by visitors from around the world. The faithful, and there are many in San Miguel, move toward the open Parroquia doors at the sound of the bells.

As a foreigner, I'm a visitor here in San Miguel. As an artist, I have been given many privileges, and I feel both responsible and grateful. I am given the privilege of being an observer, the privilege of being a participant, and the privilege of being allowed to face a blank canvas, free to draw and paint what it means to be in a place of one's own desires. "Place" plays a significant and important role in determining how we feel. When asked: *Do you like it here? Do you find this to be your home? Are your friends here?* Joseph Campbell wrote, "One needs to seek that sacred place; it is essential to our being human."

In my many encounters with Mexicans, I've often noticed an upward glance followed quickly by a downward stare — as if the Mexican psyche continues to be influenced by Aztec history and the carnage of those days. Octavio Paz, in *The Labyrinth of Solitude*, expressed it this way: "The Mexican, whether young or old, *crillo* or *mestizo*, general or laborer or lawyer, seems to be a person who shuts himself away to protect himself: his face a mask and so is his smile."

My passport rests in my bureau drawer, along with enough travelers' checks to enable me to go north in style. Youthful faces look north to the border, to what is said to be a right of passage for all Mexicans. Many, of course, head north for work — to escape the abject poverty of small desolate towns, outposts on a highway that leads north to the United States. Mexicans, searching for a better life in America, must crawl through the border desert beset by insects and wild animals, hoping that they can find a way to avoid hiring a guide to help them cross the Rio Bravo, or what we call the Rio Grande. The river and the almost two-thousand-mile borders of these two countries have a history of grief.

Many Americans find a home in San Miguel, a *place* in which one can become more human. More than one writer and poet who has lived in San Miguel has expressed what it has meant in their work: "San Miguel, that magical place."

Originally from Maine, Roland Salazar Rose has lived in San Miguel de Allende for over twenty years. A prolific painter, Salazar's work has appeared in the United States, Canada, Europe, and the United Kingdom, as well as galleries in San Miguel. In 1997 he began writing a memoir of his life in art, his relationship with his father, and his father's final days in San Miguel: My Father's Room *and* The Four Seasons of the Maser Myth. *It will be published later this year. For additional details on his writing, paintings and exhibitions, see www.salazargallery.com. Salazar's studio-home, in Los Balcones, provides a splendid view of the cityscape, where flocks of white-faced Ibis fly by at sunset.*

On a Highwire in San Miguel

PEGGY PURCELL

I dreamed last night of Vitriolo,
handsome, debonair at eighty,
performing on a high wire
overhead.
Fear jolted me awake.
One misstep and he'd be gone!
In a flash I knew
I had to change his act.
Better if he could do
some soft shoe on the corner,
use a cane to keep his balance
and a top hat for the money.

I could find a shaggy little dog,
cute, coal black
with white nose, white paws,
teach him to dance on his hind legs.

They'd be a two-some
in black and white
if Vitriolo wore tails.

It's all arranged.
He's coming to San Miguel

to dance until he drops,
not very far to fall,
not very far at all.

Then we'll put him into bed,
with little Tux to keep him warm,
find a *cuidadora*
to bring breakfast and his pills.

And he'll die peacefully,
be buried in the *panteón*,
and party with the others
buried there
on the next Day of the Dead.

Peggy Purcell took early retirement from the Boston University administration in 1986 to live in Maine and took up full-time residence in San Miguel de Allende in 1995. A student of Judyth Hill's 2009 Poetry Workshop, she was inspired to start writing memoir episodes in poetry and developed her own story-telling style. Pudding House Publications published her first collection, Roots and Seeds: tales from a farmer's daughter, *due to its fresh voice, the detail of Indiana farm life, and Peggy's life experiences.* Roots and Seeds *recounts stories from 1931 to the present.*